Peter Gilbert

ALL ABOUT
THE UNIVERSE

Here is an introduction to the great new discoveries made possible as men and their instruments peer farther and farther out into space. David Dietz, Pulitzer Prize winner and member of the American Astronomical Society, concludes this book by presenting the chief theories about the nature and origin of the universe, including the "big-bang" theory and the "steady-state" theory.

ALL
ABOUT

THE
UNIVERSE

by David Dietz

illustrated with diagrams by
JOHN POLGREEN
and with photographs

allabout
books

RANDOM
HOUSE
NEW·YORK

For helpful suggestions in the preparation of this book, the author and publisher are grateful to Dr. J. J. Nassau, Professor of Astronomy, Case Institute of Technology; Dr. Peter van de Kamp, Director, Sproul Observatory, Swarthmore College; and Dr. Lloyd Motz, Professor of Astronomy, Columbia University.

PHOTOGRAPH CREDITS: *Aerofilms and Aero Pictorial Ltd.*, 101; *California Institute of Technology*, 8, 130; *Case Institute of Technology, Cleveland*, 20; *The Cleveland Press*, 15; *Cornell University*, 100 bottom; *Ralph Crane (from Black Star)*, 7; *J. R. Eyerman*, 96, 109; *Harvard University News Office*, 77; *Theodore E. Houck and Arthur D. Code, University of Wisconsin*, 79; *Lick Observatory, University of California*, ii-iii, 24 right, 49, 55; *Mount Wilson and Palomar Observatories*, vi, 4, 17, 30, 31, 33, 37, 38, 51, 56, 62, 84, 85, 86, 91, 105, 110, 126; *National Aeronautics and Space Administration*, 25; *Alan W. Richards*, 114; *Dr. Martin Schwarzschild, Princeton University Observatory*, 36; *University News Bureau, Ithaca, N.Y.*, 100 top; *Yerkes Observatory, University of Chicago*, 14, 24 left, 28, 81, 93.

Cover photograph copyrighted 1959 by the California Institute of Technology. Endpapers: Lick Observatory.

All rights reserved under International and Pan-American Copyright Conventions. Published in New York by Random House, Inc., and simultaneously in Toronto, Canada by Random House of Canada Limited.

Library of Congress Catalog Card Number: 63-11950

Manufactured in the United States of America

2 865

Dedicated to my constellation

JAMES	MITZI
ROBERT	PAUL
JACQUELYN	DANIEL

DAVID III

CONTENTS

ALL ABOUT
THE UNIVERSE

1

The giant eye

The biggest eye in the world is on a mountain in California. It is the great 200-inch telescope of the Palomar Observatory, the most powerful telescope on earth.

Palomar Mountain is one of the broad peaks in the magnificent ranges of mountains that parallel the Pacific Coast. It is 100 miles southeast of Los Angeles and about 50 miles north of San Diego.

A trip to the observatory takes you through rolling hills, past groves of orange, grapefruit, avocado, and walnut trees. Beyond are the great greenish-brown mountains, a few of them snow-capped.

Palomar Mountain is a little more than a mile high—6,100 feet to be exact. The road up it is an excellent one. From its top you get a breath-taking view of a series of mountain ranges extending to the coast. Green valleys alternate with the dark towering mountains, some of which are shrouded in fog. And beyond them you catch the glint of sunlight on the waters of the Pacific Ocean.

The observatory is located on a plateau near the top of the mountain at an altitude of 5,600 feet. There are three domes, each housing a telescope, and some smaller buildings.

Your attention is quickly drawn to the largest structure, the huge dome of the 200-inch telescope. It seems to grow out of the ground, a true brother to the mountain on which it stands. It is 137 feet in

diameter and 135 feet high, as high as a 12-story building.

The rotating part of the dome is a huge hemisphere of steel, weighing 1,000 tons. It is mounted on wheels and turned by electric motors. A long slot in it can be closed by shutters when the telescope is not in use.

When you enter the dome, you notice that the whole interior of the dome is lined with gleaming sheets of aluminum. The mighty telescope rises from the center of the floor. It is supported on a gigantic framework of steel girders that goes down to concrete piers sunk in the granite surface of the mountain.

A huge steel cradle or yoke, known as the *polar axis,* is suspended on this framework. It weighs 200 tons. It is tilted so that it parallels the earth's axis, its upper end always pointing at the North Star. It is mounted on two bearings so that it can turn in an east-west direction.

The telescope tube is hung in this cradle on spindles which permit it to move in a north-south direction. The tube is really no tube at all but an open eight-sided framework of steel girders, 55 feet long and 22 feet in diameter. It weighs 40 tons.

The mirror is in a circular steel cell at the bottom of the octagonal framework. It is 200 inches in diameter—almost 17 feet. The surface has been so carefully ground and polished that the deviation of any spot from the desired curvature is less than a millionth of an inch. The surface is coated with a thin film of aluminum which is superior to silver and stays bright longer.

At the top of the octagonal framework there is a smaller steel

The dome of the 200-inch telescope on Palomar Mountain. Its shutters can be closed when the telescope is not in use.

5

tube, about 10 feet long and 6 feet in diameter. The upper end of this tube forms the observer's cage.

When the telescope is pointed at a star, the light comes down the open octagonal framework, strikes the mirror at the bottom, and is reflected upward to a focus at the observer's cage. Here the astronomer examines the image with the aid of an eyepiece or records it on a photographic plate.

The fact that the astronomer sits inside the 200-inch telescope is one of the most amazing things about it. If you have used a small telescope, you know how careful you must be. If you brush against the eyepiece, you knock the telescope out of adjustment. But the massive framework of the giant telescope is so huge that your weight makes no more difference than that of a fly crawling around on one of its girders.

A few weeks after the giant telescope was completed, I was invited to inspect it and to go for a ride in the observer's cage. I wondered if I should have been trained as a steeplejack. But actually it was quite simple.

A little railed platform, like the bridge of a ship, juts out from the wall of the dome. I stepped on this bridge with my guide and he pushed a button.

The bridge started up the wall of the observatory, rising up a track by means of an electrical hoisting mechanism.

Meanwhile, the engineer at the control desk of the telescope pushed a button which put the telescope in motion so that it swung in the direction of our bridge. When the observer's cage was ex-

The man at the lower right is dwarfed by the giant telescope. The observer's cage is at the upper left.

The author in the observer's cage, 50 feet above the "giant eye."

actly opposite the bridge, the engineer brought both to rest.

All I had to do then was to open the gate at the end of the bridge, get a firm grip on one of the crossbars of the cage, and step across the intervening space, resolutely keeping my mind off the fact that the floor of the observatory was seven stories below me.

Once in the top of the telescope, I settled myself comfortably in the observer's seat. In front of me were the eyepiece and the plate-holder.

The engineer pushed another button and the telescope swung away from the bridge. Overhead, through the slot in the dome, were the star-filled heavens whose mysteries this great telescope had been built to probe.

Looking upward, I felt that I had taken off in a space ship and sailed out among the stars. And, indeed, this mighty telescope is a kind of space ship, enabling the astronomer to journey far beyond our solar system, far beyond the stars of the Milky Way, to distant reaches of the universe.

Often an astronomer will spend a whole night in the observer's cage, taking photographs of a distant cluster of stars or a galaxy. Very distant objects are so faint that the photographic plate must be exposed for several hours to record them.

The astronomers who use the 200-inch telescope do not live on Palomar Mountain. In Pasadena, near Los Angeles, there is a joint headquarters for the Palomar Observatory and the Mt. Wilson Observatory.

The astronomers journey from the headquarters to Palomar or to Mt. Wilson, where there is a 100-inch telescope, to make their photographs. Then they take them back to Pasadena for detailed study. Often an astronomer will spend a month, or even a year, studying the pictures he took in one night.

Long hours of patient work, not only by the Palomar and Mt. Wilson astronomers but by astronomers at observatories all over the world, have resulted in our present picture of the nature and structure of the universe. Many mysteries have been solved but many others remain. As you read this book, astronomers in all parts of the world are wrestling with them.

2

Telescopes

For thousands of years men could see no more in the heavens than was apparent to the unaided eye. They had no way of knowing what the sun or moon or planets or stars were really like. Then, in the year 1609, the great Italian scientist Galileo turned a little telescope upon the sky.

One surprising discovery after another met his gaze as he studied the heavens. His telescope revealed the mountains on the moon. Most astonishing of all, it disclosed four tiny moons revolving around the planet Jupiter.

As he studied the stars, he noted many too faint to be seen without the telescope. And he discovered that the Milky Way, which appears to the unaided eye like a luminous streak of cloud, is actually composed of myriads of stars.

Galileo was not the inventor of the telescope. The telescope had been invented in Holland some time before. It is not quite certain who made the first one, but the credit is usually given to an optician named Hans Lippershey. According to legend, he happened to hold up two spectacle lenses, one in front of the other. Looking through them, he noticed that they made a distant church steeple seem closer.

Galileo heard about the invention in 1609 and decided to make a telescope himself. He made his first little instrument by fitting a spectacle lens in either end of an organ pipe. It was not very good and magnified only three times. He began to grind and polish his own lenses and soon constructed a telescope that magnified 33 times. It was with this instrument that he made his famous discoveries in 1609 and 1610. In Florence, Italy, you can see two of his telescopes which have been preserved in the Science Museum in that city.

In all of his telescopes, Galileo used a convex lens at the far end of the tube for the *objective*, as it is called, and a concave lens for an *eyepiece*. (A *convex* lens is thicker at the center than at the edges; a *concave* lens is thinner at the center.) The concave eyepiece merely passed on the converging rays of light from the convex lens.

Another famous astronomer, Johann Kepler, who lived at the same time as Galileo, saw that the telescope could be greatly improved by permitting the light from the objective to come to a focus and then using another convex lens as an eyepiece. This eyepiece now acted as a magnifying glass to magnify the image.

However, the early telescope builders soon ran into a difficulty. When they built bigger telescopes, they found that the images were no longer sharp but blurred with the colors of the rainbow. This was because white light is a mixture of all the colors of the rainbow and the different colors were not brought to one sharp focus.

A Scotch mathematician named James Gregory in 1663 suggested a telescope which used a concave mirror as the objective to gather the light and bring it to a focus. The first telescope of this sort was built by the great English mathematician Sir Isaac New-

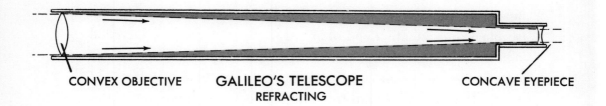

CONVEX OBJECTIVE   **GALILEO'S TELESCOPE**   CONCAVE EYEPIECE
REFRACTING

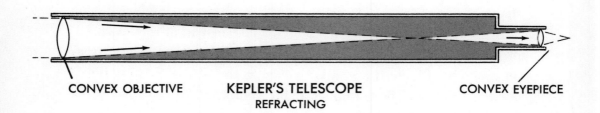

CONVEX OBJECTIVE   **KEPLER'S TELESCOPE**   CONVEX EYEPIECE
REFRACTING

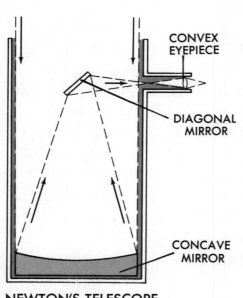

CONVEX
EYEPIECE

DIAGONAL
MIRROR

CONCAVE
MIRROR

NEWTON'S TELESCOPE
REFLECTING

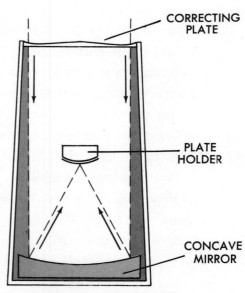

CORRECTING
PLATE

PLATE
HOLDER

CONCAVE
MIRROR

SCHMIDT-TYPE TELESCOPE
REFLECTING

ton in 1671. It was a very small telescope employing a mirror only one inch in diameter.

Newton's telescope used a second flat mirror to reflect the image into the eyepiece which was placed at one side at the top of the tube.

Telescopes built on Newton's plan became known as *reflecting telescopes* or *reflectors*. Those which follow Kepler's plan are called *refracting telescopes* or *refractors*.

Eventually, telescope makers learned to get sharp images with refracting telescopes. This was done by using an objective which was a combination of two lenses made of two different kinds of glass.

Today, both refractors and reflectors are in use. The largest refractor is the 40-inch telescope at the Yerkes Observatory in Wisconsin.

The very biggest telescopes are all reflectors. The largest reflectors are the 84-inch telescope at the McDonald Observatory in Texas, the 84-inch telescope at the Kitt Peak National Observatory in Arizona, the 100-inch telescope at the Mt. Wilson Observatory, the 104-inch telescope of the Crimean Observatory in Russia, the 120-inch telescope of the Lick Observatory on Mt. Hamilton in California, and of course, the largest of them all, the 200-inch telescope on Palomar Mountain.

The bigger a refracting or reflecting telescope, the farther it will see into space. But these big telescopes have one drawback. They see only a very small area of the sky at one time. Scientists say they have a small field of view. The more powerful the telescope, the smaller the field of view.

Modern astronomers felt the need of telescopes with larger fields of view to make it easier to survey the heavens. The problem was solved by a German optician named Bernhard Schmidt in 1931. He invented a modified reflecting telescope which is known as the Schmidt-type telescope.

The Schmidt-type telescope has a concave mirror at the bottom of the tube. But before the light reaches the mirror, it passes through a very thin lens known as the *correcting plate*.

The correcting plate bends the rays of light so that the telescope brings a large area of the sky into sharp focus on the photographic plate.

The 40-inch telescope at Yerkes Observatory, largest refractor in the world.

A small telescope can be fun. This is a 4-inch refractor.

The astronomer does not look through the telescope but sights through a smaller telescope, known as a *guiding telescope* or *finder*, attached to it. Similar auxiliary telescopes are also attached to refracting and reflecting telescopes to make it easier to focus on a desired object.

At Palomar Mountain there is a Schmidt-type telescope with a correcting plate 48 inches in diameter. This instrument will provide a sharp photograph of an area of the sky 1,000 times as large as can be seen through the 200-inch telescope. The Palomar Observatory also has a smaller Schmidt-type telescope with a correcting plate 18 inches in diameter.

Astronomers have talked about telescopes even larger than the giant eye on Palomar Mountain. Perhaps someday a 300-inch telescope will be built.

3

The spectroscope

The telescope alone could never have revealed all we know about the universe today. Much of our knowledge is due to a wonderful instrument called the *spectroscope*.

A telescope will locate a distant star and tell us about its brightness and color. But the spectroscope will tell us its chemical composition, the behavior of the gases in its atmosphere, and whether it is moving toward us or away from us.

The heart of the spectroscope is a triangular glass prism. If such a prism is held up to the sunlight, it will spread the beam of white light into a rainbow of colors from red to violet. Scientists call this little rainbow a *spectrum*. It was Newton who first demonstrated that white light is a mixture of all the colors of the rainbow, and that the prism bends the different colors by different amounts, thus spreading them out into a rainbow.

The colors differ from each other because of the wave lengths of their light. Red light has the longest waves, violet light the shortest. The prism sorts out the different wave lengths.

Newton admitted a ray of sunlight into a darkened room through a hole in the window shutter and used a prism to form a spectrum on the opposite wall. More than a century later, in the year 1815, a German scientist named Joseph von Fraunhofer made an exciting

16

discovery. He placed a little telescope behind the prism. In this way he could examine a magnified image of the sun's spectrum. To his surprise, he found that it was crossed by hundreds of dark lines. He counted more than 500 of them.

Almost half a century more went by before the riddle of these dark lines was solved. This was done by two German scientists, Gustav Kirchhoff and Robert Bunsen. They showed that each chemical element, when vaporized in a gas flame, furnishes a spectrum which is a series of bright lines. Each line is a particular wave length of light. But when the light from a very hot source is permitted to shine through the glowing vapor, the resulting spectrum is a rainbow in which dark lines replace the former bright lines. In other words, each chemical element absorbs and removes from the rainbow the wave lengths of light which it normally produces.

Here then was the explanation of the sun's spectrum. Light from the surface of the sun passes through the cooler gases of the sun's atmosphere. The dark lines in the sun's spectrum reveal the chemi-

How do astronomers know there is iron in the sun, more than ninety million miles away? They match the spectrum of iron (obtained in a laboratory) with part of the sun's spectrum (obtained with a telescope). Here the sun's spectrum is in the middle with the iron spectrum above and below.

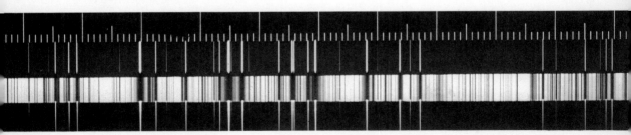

cal elements in the sun's atmosphere.

The apparatus which Kirchhoff and Bunsen used was an improvement on Fraunhofer's arrangement, which had become known as a spectroscope.

Light is admitted to the prism through a slit at the end of a small tube, which contains a lens for making parallel the rays from the light source. In addition, there is a little telescope to provide a magnified image of the spectrum.

Astronomers make use of the spectroscope today by attaching it to a telescope in place of the eyepiece. The image of the star, formed by the telescope, falls on the slit of the spectroscope. Usually the eyepiece of the spectroscope is replaced by a photographic plate so that a permanent record of the spectrum is obtained. A spectroscope equipped to make such a picture is called a *spectrograph*.

A spectroscope. The rays of light admitted through the slit are made parallel by the convex lens. The prism spreads the light into a spectrum of colors, magnified by the telescope.

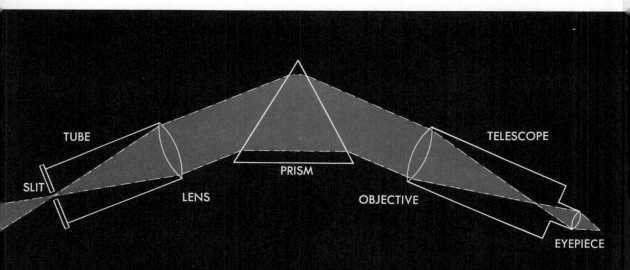

Often the prisms are replaced by a piece of glass or metal on which hundreds of parallel lines have been ruled very close together. Such a surface reflects the different wave lengths of light at different angles and thus forms a spectrum.

The lines in the spectrum of a star not only reveal the chemical elements in its outer region but also tell their temperature and electrical state.

Another important fact is also revealed by the lines. Perhaps you have noticed that the pitch of an automobile horn rises as the auto approaches, and falls as it recedes. This is known as the *Doppler effect,* after the scientist who first noticed it. The pitch rises as the auto approaches because the sound waves are being crowded on each other. More of them reach your ear per second than if the auto was standing still. As a result, the pitch goes up. As the auto recedes, fewer sound waves reach your ear per second and the pitch goes down.

The same thing happens to the light of the stars. If a star is approaching the earth, the light waves are crowded on each other. This increases the frequency of the light reaching the earth. As a result the spectrum lines are shifted a little toward the violet end of the spectrum. If the star is receding, just the opposite happens and the lines are shifted toward the red end of the spectrum. By measuring the shift, astronomers can calculate the speed with which the star is moving.

Astronomers also make use of another technique which was invented by Fraunhofer. To study the spectra of stars, he placed a fairly large prism in front of the lens of a four-inch telescope. When he looked in the eyepiece, he saw a little spectrum instead of the image of the star.

Today a very large prism is often placed in front of a telescope, particularly a Schmidt-type telescope. Such a prism, known as an *objective prism*, turns every star into a little spectrum. As a result, the astronomer can photograph dozens of spectra, even several hundred, on one photographic plate.

About 150 years ago a great French philosopher, Auguste Comte, rashly predicted that man would never know what the stars are made of. The spectroscope made possible the miracle which he thought could never happen.

Dr. J. J. Nassau puts the objective prism in place on the 24-inch Schmidt telescope at Case Institute of Technology.

4

The moon

The moon is an object of ever-changing beauty. Sometimes we see it as a thin crescent in the western sky at sunset. As twilight deepens, the crescent grows brighter and brighter until it gleams like silver. At other times, it comes over the eastern horizon like a great golden ball, lighting up the landscape with a soft radiance.

In ancient times many myths were created to explain why the moon went through its phases from new moon to first quarter, to full moon, to last quarter, and back again to new moon. Today, we know that the apparent change is due to two factors. One is that the moon is a satellite of the earth, revolving around it. The other is that the moon is a dark body, shining only by reflected sunlight. Its appearance depends entirely on how much of the lighted side we see.

When we see only a little of the lighted side, the moon appears as a thin crescent. It grows fatter each night as we see more of the lighted side, until finally it is full moon. Then it grows thinner again until new moon is reached.

The moon is our nearest neighbor in space. It revolves around the earth in a somewhat flattened orbit at an average distance of about 240,000 miles. As distances go in astronomy, the moon is in our back yard. It is the only astronomical object whose distance from us is measured in thousands of miles. The sun and planets are millions of miles from us. The stars are trillions of miles away.

The moon turns on its axis in exactly the same length of time that it goes around the earth. As a result it always keeps the same face turned toward the earth. The first view of the other side was obtained by Lunik III, the Russian lunar probe launched on October 4, 1959. It photographed the far side of the moon and sent the pictures back by television. Although the pictures were not very clear, they showed that the other side of the moon is much like the side we do see.

The moon has a diameter of 2,160 miles, a little more than one-fourth that of the earth. The force of gravity on the moon is only one-sixth of that on the earth. A person who weighed 120 pounds on earth would weigh only 20 pounds on the moon. If you can jump up 4 feet on the earth, you would be able to leap to a height of 24 feet on the moon.

A small telescope or binoculars reveal a surprising amount of detail on the moon. Even opera glasses show some detail not apparent to the unaided eye.

When you look at the full moon with the unaided eye, you see a pattern of light and dark areas that seem to form a face. For many centuries men have called it the "man in the moon." When Galileo turned his first little telescope on the moon, he thought the dark areas were bodies of water and so he called them *maria*, the Latin word for "seas." Today we know that there is neither air nor water on the moon. The majority of the maria are roughly circular, and in many cases they are bordered by rugged mountain ranges. The maria have been given fanciful names like Mare Serenitatis (Sea of Serenity) and Mare Imbrium (Sea of Rains).

There are 10 great mountain ranges on the visible side of the moon. Three of them, known as the lunar Alps, Apennines, and Caucasus, form the western border of the Mare Imbrium. The lunar Apennines extend in a great curve for almost 650 miles and contain more than 3,000 tall peaks, some of them 20,000 feet high.

The most spectacular features of the moon's surface are the craters and walled plains. More than 30,000 can be counted on the face of the moon which we see. These are circular pits surrounded by high mountainous walls. The craters range from some only a few thousand feet in diameter to others 70 to 80 miles in diameter. As a rule the depth of the crater below the surrounding territory matches the height of the mountain wall. The larger craters may have floors as much as two miles below the surrounding territory while the wall rises to a height of two miles. In the case of many craters, one or more mountain peaks rise from the center of the floor. The walled plains resemble craters but are larger. The largest has a diameter of 150 miles.

Other features of the lunar surface include great cracks known as *rills*. These are sometimes a mile or two in width.

Most mysterious of all the lunar features are the *rays*. These are bright streaks, radiating from some of the larger craters, which become visible at the time of full moon.

Two theories have been advanced to account for the surface features of the moon. One theory holds that the maria are solidified lakes of lava that welled up from the moon's interior, and that the craters are extinct volcanoes.

According to the other theory, the surface features were all created by the impact of meteorites that crashed into the lunar surface several billion years ago. At the present time many astronomers believe that some of the craters were created by the impact of

meteors and that others were the result of volcanic action.

Because the moon turns so slowly on its axis, any given area of the moon has two weeks of sunlight followed by two weeks of darkness. During the long day the temperature of the lunar surface goes up to about that of boiling water, 212 degrees Fahrenheit. During the long night the temperature drops to 243 degrees below zero.

Ranger 7, the American spacecraft which crashed into the moon on July 31, 1964, sent back pictures by television up until the moment of impact. These showed many small craters never before seen, some of them only three feet in diameter. Some astronomers had thought that the surface of the moon is covered with a layer of dust many feet in thickness. However the small craters in the

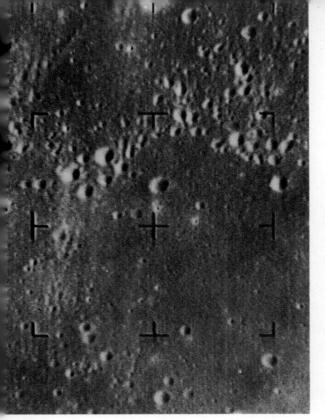

Three photographs of the moon. The two on the facing page were taken through telescopes. At left: The moon a few days after full moon. At right: Part of the lunar Apennines. Below the mountains is part of the Mare Imbrium. The large crater below the mountains is Archimedes.

On this page is a photograph taken by Ranger 7 only 35 miles from the lunar surface.

Ranger 7 pictures are so sharp that astronomers are now certain that this is not so.

Before long the first explorers will land their space ship on the moon. They will find themselves in a land far different from our earth. They will find no pleasant lakes or streams, no majestic forests or green fields. They will find only barren mountains, craters, and maria.

Shining in the sky, the moon looks like a fairyland. But the explorers will find it a hostile world, barren and lifeless, without air or water, boiling hot in the daytime and far colder than the Antarctic icecap at night.

5

The solar system

In ancient times men believed that the earth was flat and that the sky was a real dome or canopy over the earth. Today, we know that our earth is just one of nine planets that revolve around the sun.

The planets, in order from the sun, are Mercury, Venus, Earth, Mars, Jupiter, Saturn, Uranus, Neptune, and Pluto. (Numerical data about the planets are summarized in Table I in the Appendix.)

Astronomers call the first four the *terrestrial* planets, because they are all more or less like the earth. The next four are called the *major* planets because they are all larger than the earth. This leaves Pluto in a class by itself.

Mercury and Venus have no moons. Our earth has one. But Mars has two, Jupiter twelve, Saturn nine, Uranus five, and Neptune two. Pluto has no moon.

There is a wide gap between the terrestrial and major planets—that is, between Mars and Jupiter. Many thousands of tiny planets known as the *asteroids* are in this gap. They may be the remnants of a planet that exploded or fell apart in some way. It is also possible that they are material which failed to form a planet when the solar system took shape.

In addition, the solar system includes billions of comets and a vast amount of meteoric material ranging in size from particles of dust to grains of sand.

Mercury is the smallest of the planets as well as the one which is closest to the sun. It is only a little larger than our own moon.

It turns once upon its axis in the same length of time it goes around the sun. As a result, it always keeps the same face turned toward the sun. The sunlit face has a temperature of 770 degrees Fahrenheit, a temperature that is sufficient to melt tin and lead. The other side has a temperature of about 60 degrees.

Venus, the second planet in order from the sun, has been called the earth's twin sister because it is just about the same size as the earth. However, astronomers are certain that conditions on the planet are very different from those on earth. The planet is covered with a layer of clouds so thick that we never see the surface of the planet. All we see in the telescope is the outer surface of the clouds.

The portion of the atmosphere above the cloud layer contains an immense amount of carbon dioxide, very little water vapor, and almost no oxygen, perhaps none at all.

Mariner II, the U.S. space probe which passed near Venus on December 14, 1962, revealed that the planet has a surface temperature of about 800 degrees Fahrenheit. This is much too hot for life as we know it.

The earth is next in order from the sun. Then comes Mars. Even a small telescope reveals that Mars is an object of surprising beauty. The planet as a whole has a reddish or orange color. However, an irregular belt running across the middle of the planet is darker in color, having bluish-gray, bluish-green, and greenish shades. The white polar caps are seen easily with even a very small telescope.

The reddish areas show very little change with the Martian seasons. Most astronomers are inclined to think that they are great rocky or sandy deserts.

Changes in the dark areas are very marked and go through a regular cycle in the course of the Martian year. Many astronomers feel that these seasonal changes may be due to vegetation which appears in spring and withers away in autumn.

MARS

The polar caps also change with the season, growing smaller in summer and larger again in winter. The speed with which they change has convinced astronomers that they are not ice fields like our own Arctic regions but merely thin layers of snow, perhaps only two or three inches thick.

At one time, some astronomers thought that they saw a network of fine lines on Mars. The first astronomer to suggest this was an Italian, Giovanni Schiaparelli, in 1889. The lines became known as the "canals of Mars." Most astronomers today think that the fine markings are a confused hodgepodge and that the idea that they form straight lines is an optical illusion.

Spectroscopic studies show that the planet has very little atmosphere. It probably contains less than one-tenth of 1 per cent of the amount of water vapor in the earth's atmosphere, and probably an even smaller percentage of the amount of oxygen in the earth's atmosphere. However, it contains twice as much carbon dioxide.

Jupiter, when viewed with even a small telescope, looks like a golden disk crossed by light and dark bands or belts.

The equatorial belt is bright, ranging in color from pale yellow to dull red. Above and below are darker belts, ranging from reddish-brown to bluish-gray. Other belts cover the planet's surface to the north and south.

Astronomers are certain that the belts are the outer surface of dense clouds. It is impossible to see through them.

Many astronomers think that Jupiter is composed almost entirely of hydrogen, the lightest of the chemical elements, with some helium and a trace of the other chemical elements. They think that the planet has a core of frozen, solidified hydrogen. This is covered with a universal ocean of liquid hydrogen. The planet's atmosphere is gaseous hydrogen, while the clouds are composed of two other gases, ammonia and methane.

The other major planets are believed to resemble Jupiter in composition and structure. Like Jupiter, the disk of Saturn is marked with belts. The equatorial zone of Saturn has a bright yellowish color, while the polar regions are greenish.

The most amazing feature of Saturn is the system of rings. Galileo saw that there was something strange about Saturn but his little telescope was not powerful enough to make out the rings. The

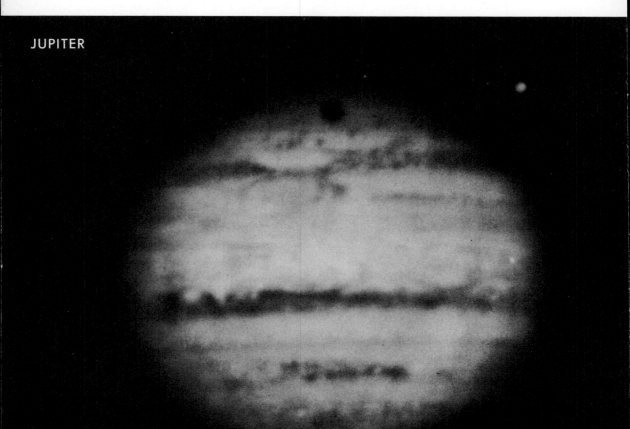

JUPITER

mystery was solved in 1656 by a Dutch astronomer, Christian Huygens. The rings are not solid but consist of millions of tiny objects, each one a tiny moon or moonlet, all of them revolving around the planet in the ring-shaped formations. It is thought that each one has a rocky core surrounded by a layer of ice and frozen gases.

Uranus and Neptune both have a distinctive greenish hue in the telescope.

Pluto, the outermost planet of the solar system, resembles the terrestrial planets. Some astronomers think that it was originally a moon of Neptune and that in some way it escaped from the gravitational pull of Neptune.

Astronomers expect to learn more about the planets in the next few years with unmanned space probes. Before the end of the present century—in less than 35 years—the first explorers will probably land on Mars.

6

The sun

We have two reasons for our interest in the sun. The first is that life on earth depends upon the sun. Therefore, we want to know what goes on in the sun and how it affects the earth. The other is that the sun is a star, a typical star. Consequently, whatever we learn about the sun helps us to understand the other stars in the universe. It is the only star we can study in detail.

The sun is a gigantic globe of glowing gas with a diameter almost 110 times that of the earth. The diameter of the sun is 864,600 miles. It would take 1,300,000 globes, each of the size of the earth, to equal the volume of the sun.

The surface temperature of the sun is about 10,000 degrees Fahrenheit. But the interior of the sun is much hotter. The temperature at the center of the sun is about 27 million degrees.

For a long time scientists wondered where the sun got its vast supply of energy. We now know that the center of the sun is a great atomic furnace. Its energy comes from the conversion of hydrogen into helium, the same transformation that takes place in the hydrogen bomb. Four hydrogen atoms combine to form one helium atom. When this happens there is a loss in mass. The mass that disappears is converted into energy.

This conversion of mass into energy was first pointed out by the

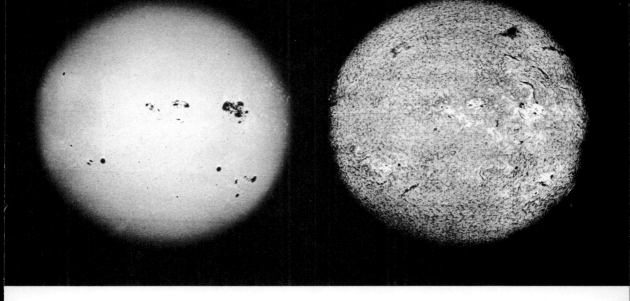

Left: A direct photograph of the sun, showing the photosphere and sunspots. Right: A photograph taken with a spectroheliograph (a solar telescope with spectroscope attached). Taken in the light of one line of the hydrogen spectrum, the photograph shows the hydrogen clouds in the sun's chromosphere.

famous scientist Albert Einstein. He expressed it in the equation $E = mc^2$. This means that the amount of energy produced is equal to the amount of mass that is lost multiplied by the square of the velocity of light.

Thus the sun is losing mass as it pours out its immense flood of radiation. Physicists have calculated that the sun loses four million tons a second.

Astronomers are certain that the sun will go on shining for at least five billion years. This is very lucky for us.

Were the sun to go out, the earth would be plunged into eternal darkness. We would see the stars, but not the moon or planets which shine by reflected sunlight. The air would quickly begin to grow very chilly. Within a week the tropics would be as cold as the North Pole and the whole earth would be snowbound. Soon the oceans would freeze to their lowest depths. Then the atmosphere would freeze, forming first a layer of liquid air on the frozen surface of the earth, finally a layer of solid air.

At sunrise or sunset, the sun is sometimes dimmed so much by the earth's atmosphere that one can safely look at it. But no one should ever look directly at the sun when it is higher in the sky. Opera glasses or binoculars should never be pointed at it. Serious damage to the eyes, even blindness, can result. A telescope should

A cross-section of the sun

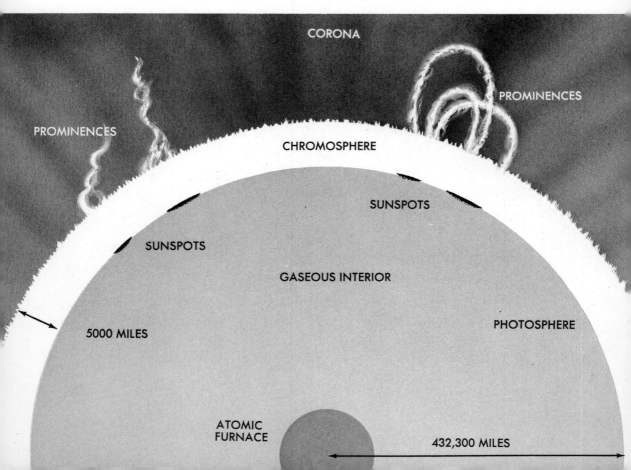

never be pointed at the sun unless it is equipped with a proper and safe solar eyepiece. Astronomers use special types of telescopes to study the sun.

The surface of the sun is a seething, boiling sea of glowing gases, constantly churning with unbelievable fury. The solar atmosphere is the scene of even greater turmoil.

The restless surface of the sun is called the *photosphere*. The telescope reveals that it has a mottled or speckled appearance. It consists of bright granules separated by darker lanes. The scene is constantly changing, old granules disappearing in a matter of minutes and new ones taking their place. Their behavior resembles that of the bubbles on a boiling pot. Astronomers are certain that the granules are bubbles of gas rising from the interior of the sun, gigantic bubbles whose diameters range from 300 to 900 miles.

The most noticeable features of the solar surface are the dark spots known as *sunspots*. They are gigantic whirlpools in the photosphere. They look dark because the gases in them are cooler than the photosphere.

Many of the spots appear and disappear in 24 hours. But if they grow large they may last a week or two, or even longer.

By watching sunspots move across the face of the sun, astronomers learned that the sun turns on its axis. However, it does not rotate like a solid body. The equatorial region turns once in 25 days, but the regions nearer the poles turn slower.

The number of spots varies from year to year, going from minimum to maximum and back to minimum in a cycle of approximately eleven years.

The sun's atmosphere becomes visible during a total solar eclipse. Then the moon blots out the photosphere, leaving the

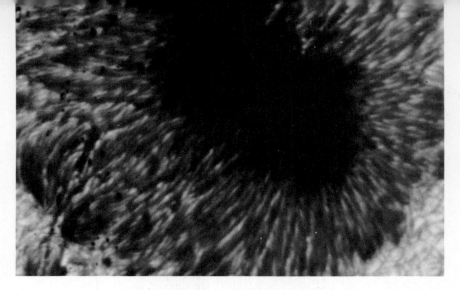

A sunspot photographed from a balloon 80,000 feet above the earth. Cooler gases form the dark core, which is surrounded by outward-moving filaments of warmer gases.

atmosphere projecting beyond its edge. As a result, a total solar eclipse is a spectacular and thrilling sight.

At the instant of totality, the sky grows dark, the stars become visible, and the dark disk of the moon appears to be rimmed with rose-colored fire beyond which pearly streamers form a great silvery halo.

The rim of rose-colored fire is the inner portion of the sun's atmosphere. It is called the *chromosphere*. Flamelike tongues rise from it. These are known as *prominences*. The silvery halo is the outer portion of the sun's atmosphere. It is called the *corona*.

The chromosphere is a layer of gases, chiefly hydrogen and helium, several thousand miles high. It is a region of tremendous winds and storms of such magnitude as to defy the imagination.

Thousands of spikes, known as *spicules*, project upward from the

The sun's corona becomes visible during a total eclipse.

chromosphere. They are the tops of columns of gas rising above the granulations of the photosphere. Like the granules, they are short-lived, new ones appearing as old ones disappear.

Far more spectacular than the spicules are the prominences. These are great gaseous clouds and streamers rising above the chromosphere to heights ranging from 10,000 miles to a million miles. Some of the prominences are relatively quiet, towering above the chromosphere in fantastic shapes. Others erupt suddenly like gigantic geysers shooting up with speeds as great as 400 miles a second.

A solar prominence 140,000 miles high. The white circle shows the relative size of the earth.

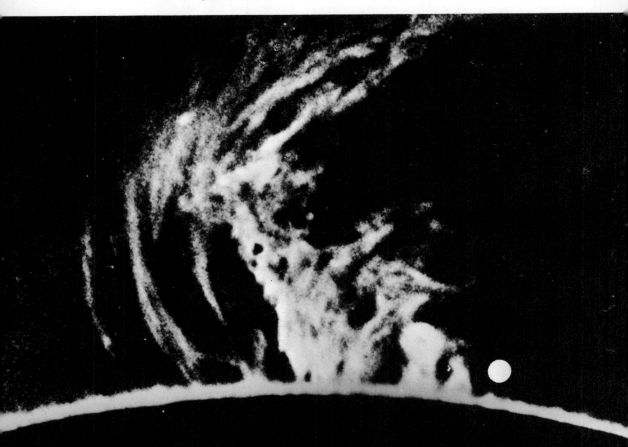

The corona has a delicate structure of fanlike rays. It consists of extremely thin, highly electrified gases.

It is now known that the sun is constantly sending a vast amount of gaseous material into space. Sudden outbreaks of intense patches of ultraviolet light on the solar surface, known as *flares,* are followed by the ejection of huge clouds and streams of gaseous material. When these streams reach the earth they cause magnetic storms that upset the compass, interfere with radio communications, and create brilliant displays of the Aurora Borealis or Northern Lights.

Many stars, perhaps one-tenth of them, are very much like our sun. Many stars are larger than the sun, but a much greater number are smaller.

7

The stars

On a clear moonless night the stars seem countless. But this is not really so. Astronomers long ago counted the stars that can be seen without instruments. About 2,000 can be seen from any one place at a given time. All told, there are about 6,000 stars visible to the unaided eye in both the northern and southern hemispheres of the earth.

With a telescope you can see many more stars. Each time a larger telescope is used, still more stars come into view. Galileo's little telescope revealed half a million stars. Many billions of stars can be seen with the 200-inch telescope on Palomar Mountain.

All the stars are so far away that they appear only as points of light in the most powerful telescopes. The nearest star is 25 trillion miles away. Many stars are more than a thousand times farther away.

When we look at the night sky, we note at once that some stars are brighter than others. The brightest stars are called *first-magnitude* stars. The next brightest are the *second magnitude,* and so on. The stars just visible to the unaided eye are the *sixth magnitude.* The scale is so arranged that there is a difference in brightness of 2½ times between magnitudes. This makes the first-magnitude stars 100 times as bright as the sixth magnitude. The 21 first-magnitude stars are listed in Table II of the Appendix.

These magnitudes are called *apparent magnitudes* because they represent the appearance of the stars. A star may appear brighter than other stars for one of two reasons. It may actually be brighter than most stars. On the other hand, it may be closer to us than most stars. Astronomers call the actual brightness of a star its *luminosity*.

The luminosity range of stars is very great. The most luminous stars are a million times brighter than the sun. The least luminous stars are a million times fainter than the sun.

A careful look at the night sky reveals that the stars differ in color as well as apparent magnitude. Some stars shine with a beautiful white light while others have a ruddy hue. These colors are more pronounced in the telescope, which shows that stars range in color from red, through orange, yellow, and white, to a brilliant blue.

This difference in color is due to a difference in surface temperature. The red stars are only red-hot. They are the coolest stars with surface temperatures of about 5,000 degrees Fahrenheit. The blue stars are blue-hot. They are the hottest stars with surface temperatures of 100,000 degrees or more.

Stars differ not only in luminosity but also in size. The largest stars have diameters 3,000 times the diameter of the sun. The smallest stars have diameters only 1/400 that of the sun. They are no larger than our own moon.

However, stars differ less in mass than in size. (The *mass* of any object is the amount of matter it contains.) The larger stars are less dense than the smaller ones. The most massive stars have about 50 times the mass of the sun, the least massive ones about 1/25.

Are there stars with all combinations of luminosity, surface temperature, size, and mass? The answer is no. Only certain com-

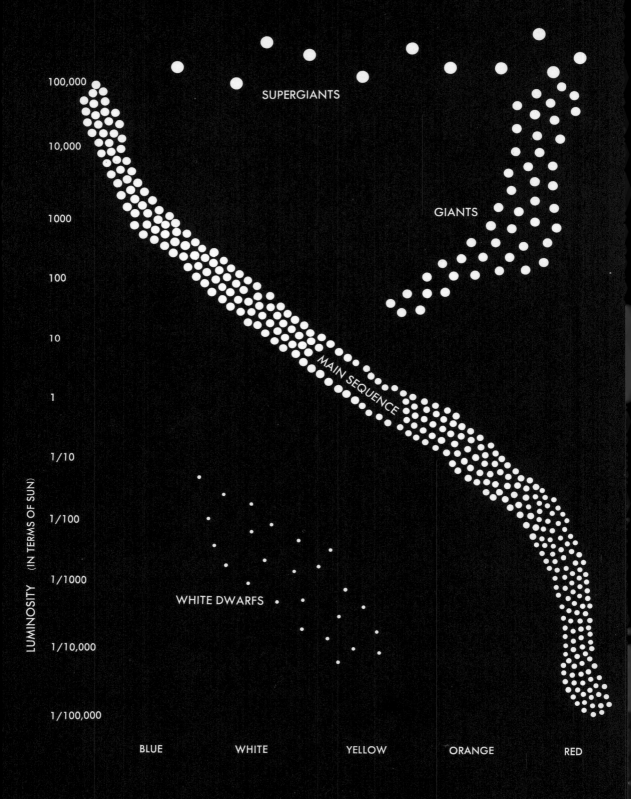

binations are found.

This was noted early in the present century by two famous astronomers, a Dane named Ejnar Hertzsprung and Henry Norris Russell of Princeton University. It can be shown most easily on a chart which astronomers call the Hertzsprung-Russell diagram or H-R diagram for short.

You will notice that the color is marked along the bottom of the diagram. Luminosity, in terms of the sun, is marked along the side.

Most of the stars fall inside a track that begins with highly luminous blue stars and runs diagonally down the diagram ending with faint red stars. This track is called the *main sequence*.

Luminosity, temperature, size and mass all grow steadily smaller from the top to the bottom of the main sequence.

At the top of the main sequence are blue stars which are 100,000 times as luminous as the sun. They have surface temperatures of about 100,000 degrees Fahrenheit. They have diameters about 20 times that of the sun and they are about 32 times as massive.

As we descend the main sequence we encounter stars that are progressively cooler. Consequently, the colors of the stars change from blue to white, yellow, orange, and finally red. At the same time the stars grow less luminous, smaller, and less massive.

At the bottom of the main sequence we find red stars that range from one-hundredth down to a ten-thousandth as luminous as the sun. They have surface temperatures of about 5,000 degrees. They have diameters about one-fourth or less than that of the sun and they are about one-fifth or less as massive.

The H-R diagram charts the stars of our galaxy according to color and luminosity. Our sun, a yellow star, falls in the center of this diagram.

The stars of the main sequence are all relatively small stars, especially the stars in the lower part. These are called *dwarf* stars. Our own sun fits into the yellow portion of the main sequence and is consequently called a *yellow dwarf* star. The red stars at the bottom of the main sequence are called *red dwarfs*.

However, not all the stars fit into the main sequence. There is another band to the right which begins near the main sequence and slopes upward to the right. This is known as the *giant sequence*. These stars are at least 10,000 times as bright as stars of corresponding color in the main sequence. Consequently, they must be very large. The diameter of a giant star is about 100 times the diameter of a main-sequence star of corresponding color. The largest stars in this sequence are red and are known as the *red giants*.

You will notice another band along the top of the H-R diagram. It consists of very rare stars of exceptional luminosity. They are called *supergiants* because they are the very largest known stars. They range in color from red to blue.

Two of the supergiant stars are Betelgeuse, the bright red star in the familiar constellation of Orion, and Antares, also a bright red star, in the constellation of Scorpio. They are about 800 million miles in diameter. If one of these stars were put in place of the sun at the center of the solar system, it would extend beyond Mercury, Venus, the earth, and Mars to the orbit of the planet Jupiter.

Finally you will notice other stars in the lower left part of the diagram. These are very small. They are known as *white dwarfs*, although some are yellow in color, and some blue.

For many centuries people spoke of the "fixed stars," taking it for granted that the stars remained fixed in their exact places in the constellations. In 1718 the British astronomer Edmund Halley, best remembered for the study of the comet named for him, showed that this is not the case. By comparing ancient records with observations made in his own day, he proved that several of the brightest stars had changed their positions slightly over the centuries. We know now that all the stars are in motion.

The constellations as we now see them look just as they did to the Greeks 2,500 years ago. But this will not be the case in the distant future. In 50,000 years many constellations as we now know them will be completely out of shape.

As we have seen, by studying the shift of the lines in the spectrum of a star, astronomers can tell whether it is moving toward us or away from us. This motion is called the *radial motion* of the star.

The motion of a star across the heavens—across the line of sight, as astronomers say—is called its *proper motion*. If we know how far away a star is, we can calculate the speed of its proper motion.

By combining the proper motion with the radial motion, we can calculate the exact direction in which a star is moving and how fast it is moving.

The stars in our part of the galaxy are moving in all directions, much like a swarm of bees. Because distances are so vast, they do not seem to us to be moving very fast. In fact, however, the majority of the stars are moving at a speed of 5 to 20 miles a second. Some are going faster. Arcturus, the bright orange star in the constellation of Boötes, has a velocity of 84 miles per second.

When we analyze the proper motions of stars in the neighborhood of the sun, we find that the stars in the direction of the constellation of Hercules appear to be opening out. Those in the opposite direction appear to be closing in. This effect is the result of the motion of our own sun, carrying the earth and the other planets along with it. Our sun is moving in the direction of the constellation of Hercules with a speed of 12 miles per second.

The stars form a gigantic system which we call the *galaxy*. Sometimes we speak of it as our galaxy because there are other galaxies at vast distances from our own. The structure of both our own galaxy and these others will be discussed in later chapters, but first let us take a closer look at some stars.

8

Double, variable, and exploding stars

When we turn a telescope upon the stars visible to the unaided eye, we make a surprising discovery. We find that many of them are not single stars but pairs of stars close together. Astronomers call them *double stars*. Many double stars have been under observation for more than a century. We now know that the two stars revolve around a common center of gravity.

Astronomers are certain that more than half of all the stars in our galaxy are twins, triplets, quadruplets, or even sextuplets. In the case of triplets, two of the stars are usually close together, with a third farther away.

Stars shown to be double by the telescope are known as *visual binaries*. But there are also double stars whose components are so close together that the telescope cannot separate them. These are known as *spectroscopic binaries* because they can be detected by the spectroscope.

The lines in the spectrum of a spectroscopic binary are double. As the two stars go around each other, one is moving toward us while the other is moving away from us. Consequently the lines of one are shifted toward the red, the other toward the violet.

Astronomers have calculated the orbits of more than a hundred double stars. Once the orbit of a double star is known, it is possible to calculate the mass of the components.

The time which two stars take to journey around their common center of gravity depends upon the distance between them. This time is known as the *period* of the double star. In the case of visual binaries, it ranges from a little less than two years to more than 700 years. Spectroscopic binaries have much shorter periods, ranging from about a year to less than 10 days.

Sometimes the components of a double star are alike, forming a pair of identical twins. However, this is not usually the case. Frequently the difference between the components is startling. Sirius, the Dog Star, is a good example of this. The brighter component has twice the diameter of the sun, is twice as massive, and has a surface temperature twice as high. It is 25 times as luminous as the sun. The other component is a white dwarf which astronomers have nicknamed "the Pup." Its diameter is about 1/50 that of the sun and it is only 1/400 as luminous.

Several hundred spectroscopic binaries are called *eclipsing variables*. They suddenly grow dim when the less luminous component passes in front of the brighter component.

There are also many single stars whose light fluctuates. Astronomers call them *variable stars*. About 10,000 have been catalogued, but there probably are millions of them in our galaxy. Most variable stars are giant or supergiant stars. They can be divided into three classes on the basis of whether their fluctuations are regular, semi-regular, or irregular.

The regular variables are pulsating stars which vary in brightness because they are alternately contracting and expanding, growing hotter and cooler by turns. They go through the cycle from minimum brightness to maximum and back again to minimum with clocklike precision. Chief among the pulsating stars are the Cepheid variables. They get their name from the fact that the first one studied was in the constellation of Cepheus. They are yellow giant stars.

The semi-regular and irregular variables are red giant and supergiant stars. Among the largest of the irregular variables is the supergiant star, Betelgeuse, in the constellation of Orion.

More spectacular than the variable stars are the exploding stars, known as *novae* and *supernovae*. The name *nova* is from the Latin for "new." It was given to them several centuries ago when it was imagined that they were really new stars that had suddenly come into existence.

We know now that a nova was always there. But it was a faint and insignificant star like the millions of other faint stars. Suddenly the star blazes up with spectacular brilliance. Astronomers are now certain that a nova is an exploding star.

Left: Nova Herculis as seen on March 10, 1935. Right: Three months later the nova has become so faint that arrows are needed to identify it.

Only a few are near enough to become visible to the unaided eye, but additional ones are found on photographic plates taken with big telescopes. It is estimated that 20 or 30 stars in our galaxy become novae each year. Novae have also been detected in some of the nearer galaxies in the universe.

Before the explosion, the nova is a small, very hot star of high density, blue in color. It is not very bright, despite its high surface temperature, because it is so small.

A sudden liberation of a vast amount of energy within the star causes it to eject a great shell of gas with explosive violence. The star does not expand, but the gaseous shell does so rapidly, attaining the diameter of a supergiant star. The nova may become 500,-000 times as bright as it was before the explosion. Some novae reach their maximum brightness in two or three days. Others may take a week or even a month. As the shell expands, it begins to grow cooler and so the nova begins to fade.

Although the explosion of a nova is extremely spectacular, astronomers calculate that it loses only about one 100,000th of its mass as a result of the explosion. Some novae have been known to explode more than once. One, which was first seen to explode in 1890, was seen to explode again in 1902, and a third time in 1920.

The explosion of a nova, gigantic as it is, is feeble by comparison with that of a supernova. A supernova is a faint star which suddenly increases about 100 million times in brightness. The supernova ejects a tremendous shell of gas that may contain as much as a tenth or more of the star's original mass.

The Crab Nebula, remains of the supernova seen in 1054 A.D.

Supernovae are very rare. Only three are known to have occurred in our galaxy in historic times. The first one appeared in the year 1054. It is recorded in the Chinese annals. The second one appeared in November 1572. It became brighter than the planet Venus and could be seen in daylight. All Europe was startled by it, and superstitious people thought it heralded the end of the world. It did not fade from view until two years later. It became known as Tycho's Nova because the great Danish astronomer, Tycho Brahe, wrote a book about it.

The third supernova appeared in October 1604. It became known as Kepler's Nova after the German astronomer, Johann Kepler, who wrote a book about it.

Astronomers of today have located the supernova of 1054. It is a white dwarf star in the constellation of Taurus, surrounded by a huge shell of gas consisting of a great tangle of bright filaments. Because of its general shape, astronomers call it the Crab Nebula. It is still expanding from the force of the explosion that was seen more than 900 years ago.

Astronomers have not been so successful in locating the supernovae of 1572 and 1604. Irregular patches of gaseous clouds, somewhat resembling the Crab Nebula, are thought to be a remnant of the supernova of 1604.

Exploding stars, as we shall see, are stars that are nearing the end of their lives.

9

The nebulae

Perhaps you are familiar with the constellation of Orion which shines so spectacularly in the winter sky. Except for the Big Dipper, it is the easiest constellation to identify. It is supposed to represent the mythological figure of Orion, the mighty hunter.

The bright red star Betelgeuse marks the shoulder of the giant, the beautiful blue star Rigel his foot. Three fairly bright stars form the "belt of Orion," and three fainter ones, the "sword of Orion." If you look carefully at the center star in the sword, you will note that it has a hazy or fuzzy appearance. This is the Great Nebula in Orion.

A big telescope reveals the true glory of the Great Nebula in Orion. It is a vast luminous cloud of marvelous beauty and grace, shining with a soft greenish hue. The central portion is brightest. The outer region is formed by majestic, curved streamers of a dimmer green.

Embedded in the center of the nebula are four bright stars and a number of fainter ones.

The nebula becomes even more awe-inspiring when we realize its size. Astronomers estimate that it is 180 trillion miles in diameter. This is about two million times the distance from the earth to the sun.

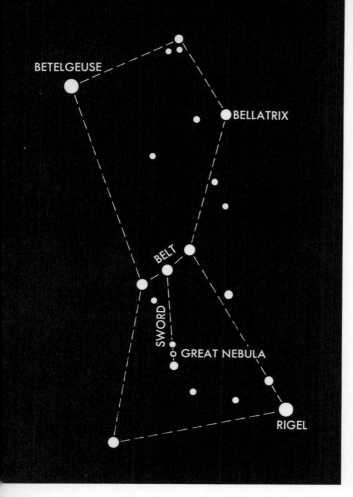

You can see the Great Nebula in Orion without instruments (left). A big telescope reveals the beauty of the Great Nebula (right).

The word *nebula* comes from a Latin word meaning "cloud" or "mist." Astronomers have listed more than a thousand nebulae in our galaxy. Each one is a vast cloud of gas and dust. Many are as large as the Great Nebula in Orion. They possess a wide variety of shapes, some extremely beautiful, others fantastic. One nebula is called the North America Nebula because it is shaped like a map of North America. Some are like delicate curtains of luminous lace draped among the stars. Not all the nebulae are luminous. Some are dark curtains, blotting the stars from view.

54

The nebulae are about 98 per cent gas, chiefly hydrogen, and only about 2 per cent dust. The dust consists of very small crystals of simple compounds of carbon, nitrogen, potassium, sodium, calcium, and so on. Many of the crystals are probably ice.

Astronomers call the luminous clouds the *diffuse* nebulae. There are one or more bright stars in or near each diffuse nebula. These stars are the source of a nebula's light.

If the star is a very hot blue star, it causes the gas to become phosphorescent so that it glows like the gas in a neon lamp. If the star is less hot, the nebula shines only by the reflection of starlight from the dust particles in the cloud.

If no star is in or near a cloud of gas and dust, it is a dark nebula. If a dark nebula happens to lie in front of a dense field of stars, we see it in silhouette. The same thing happens if it is between us and a bright nebula.

Some of the most spectacular effects are the result of combinations of bright and dark nebulae. Perhaps the best known is the Horsehead Nebula, also in the constellation of Orion. It gets its name from the fact that the dark nebula, silhouetted against the bright one, has the shape of a horse's head.

The study of the nebulae is one of the most important branches of astronomy today. It seems certain, as we shall see, that the relationship of the nebulae to the stars is one of the major keys to the understanding of the life histories of stars and the evolution of the galaxy.

This lacy diffuse nebula is stimulated into emitting visible light by the ultraviolet radiation of nearby stars.

10

Star clusters

Since ancient times, men have been captivated by the beauty of the little group of glittering stars called the Pleiades. Myths and legends were woven about them in all parts of the world. If you do not know them, you should make their acquaintance some winter evening when the sky is clear.

To the east of the constellation of Orion, the mighty hunter, you will find the constellation of Taurus, the celestial bull. Ancient star maps picture the bull with head down, charging at Orion who awaits the onslaught with upraised club.

You will note six stars which form a letter V. All of them are rather faint except one. This is the giant red star Aldebaran, which marks the right eye of the bull.

Not far from the V, you will find a compact group of six twinkling stars huddled together in a pattern about twice the size of the full moon. Their arrangement is something like a miniature version of the Big Dipper. They are the Pleiades, which are supposed to mark the shoulder of the bull.

Only six Pleiades are normally visible to the unaided eye. However, on a clear, moonless night, a person with very sharp eyes may be able to see as many as 11 or 12. Binoculars or a small tele-

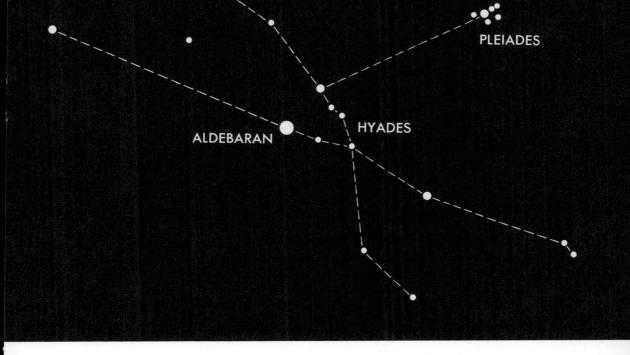

In the constellation of Taurus you can see, with the naked eye, the brightest stars of two galactic clusters.

scope will reveal 60 or so and a big telescope more than 200. The brighter stars are embedded in luminous clouds of gas and dust or diffuse nebulae, and others are entwined in luminous streamers.

The Pleiades are all moving through space in the same direction and with the same speed, like a flock of birds headed for some distant destination. They form a true family of stars. Astronomers call such a family a *galactic cluster*.

The V of stars which form the head of Taurus are part of another

59

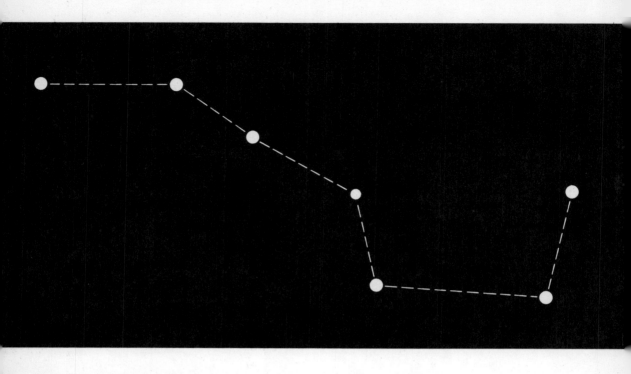

galactic cluster. A telescope reveals more than 100 stars in it. But strangely enough the giant red star Aldebaran does not belong to the cluster. It just happens to be in line with it. The cluster is twice as far from the earth as Aldebaran. It is called the Hyades.

Another galactic cluster includes five of the seven stars in the Big Dipper. The star at the end of the handle and the star at the end of the bowl do not belong to the cluster and are moving in other directions. As a result, the Big Dipper will look quite different 100,000 years from now.

The Big Dipper is only part of the constellation known as Ursa

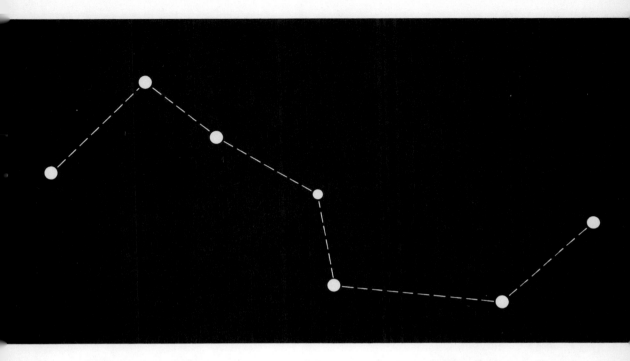

Because some of its stars move in different directions, the Big Dipper will not always retain the same shape. Left: The Big Dipper today. Right: The Big Dipper in 100,000 years.

Major or the Big Bear. The telescope reveals that the Ursa Major cluster contains more than 100 stars.

Astronomers are now aware of about 500 galactic clusters. The number of stars in each cluster varies from 20 or 30 to several hundred. A few clusters contain more than a thousand stars.

The telescope also reveals another type of cluster that is far more spectacular and awe-inspiring. These are the *globular clusters*. About a hundred of them are known.

A big telescope discloses that each globular cluster is a great formation containing from 10,000 to a million stars. The number of

stars grows greater toward the central part of the globe. The center itself is lost in a great blaze of light in which it is impossible to distinguish individual star images on photographs.

It is interesting to imagine what our sky would look like if our sun with its planets was situated inside a globular cluster. Because we would be so much closer to so many highly luminous stars, the heavens would appear far more brilliant. The brightest stars would appear as bright as the moon, and the whole sky would sparkle with very bright stars.

A globular star cluster

11

The birth and death of stars

Stars differ not only in brightness, color, surface temperature, size, and mass, but also in age. Some of the stars we see in the heavens are very young. Others are very old. Stars are being born in our galaxy today, and other stars are dying. Stars have different life spans. Some stars burn themselves out in 10 or 20 million years. Others are billions of years old and will go on shining for more billions of years.

A star, astronomers now believe, begins its life as a great cloud of gas and dust. Gravity causes the cloud to contract and assume the shape of a sphere. It is not yet a star, but only a gigantic dark globe which astronomers call a *proto-star* or *globule*.

As gravity causes the sphere to shrink more and more, it begins to grow hot. If you have ever pumped up a bicycle tire, you may have noticed that the pump got hot. This was because the temperature of the air went up as you compressed it. The same thing happens to the gas at the center of the globule. As the globule contracts, it is squeezed more and more by the outer layers of gas. It gets hotter and hotter until it is red-hot.

The globule has now become a star. It is a red star of giant size, shining dimly with irregular fluctuations in its brightness. Contraction continues, and so the center of the star grows hotter and hotter. In time, the center may reach a temperature of 10 million degrees or more. When this happens, a very important change takes place.

This temperature is high enough to make possible the atomic reaction by which hydrogen is transformed into helium. Four hydrogen atoms combine to form one helium atom. There is a loss of mass in this transformation and the loss in mass is converted into energy. You will recall that this process takes place in our sun.

The star now has a source of energy at its center. The outward push of the heated gas, and the radiations from it, balance the inward pull of gravity. The star settles down into the steady state which it will maintain for most of its life.

The size of the original cloud determines how long it takes the star to settle down and what it will be like.

If the cloud is very big, it contracts more rapidly because the force of gravity is greater. In this case it may take about 100,000 years for the star to settle down; when it does, it is a highly luminous blue or white star. A smaller cloud takes longer, becoming a less luminous yellow or red dwarf star.

When a star has settled down, it has taken its place in the main sequence. You will recall from page 42 that the great majority of stars form an array that begins with the highly luminous blue stars and ends with the small, cool stars, the red dwarfs. With the help of the H-R diagram, as shown on page 68, we can chart the evolution of a typical star.

How long a star stays in its place in the main sequence depends upon how rapidly it uses up its supply of hydrogen. As the hydrogen is converted into helium at the center of the star, a core of helium is formed. A star remains stable until it has converted all the hydrogen in its central region into helium.

You might think this would happen more quickly in a dwarf star than in a more massive blue star. But just the opposite is true. This is because the conversion of hydrogen into helium goes on so much faster in the more massive star.

A highly luminous star may remain on the main sequence for only 10 million years. It is a spendthrift star, using up its hydrogen at a tremendous rate. A less luminous star may take from 10 billion to 20 billion years to use up its hydrogen.

Once a star has used up all the hydrogen in its central region, an important change takes place. The star now begins to consume the hydrogen in the layer or shell around the helium core. The interior of the star grows hotter and hotter. The outer regions of the star begin to swell up and grow larger.

As the star expands, the surface is not only larger but farther from the central source of heat. As a result, it grows cooler and the star no longer belongs to the main sequence.

The star is now on its way to becoming a red giant. For a time, it is unstable and becomes a variable star. But eventually it becomes a red giant with a diameter a hundred times greater than the star's original diameter.

When the helium core has grown so large that it accounts for about 40 per cent of the star's mass, it begins to contract. This causes its temperature to rise to about 250 million degrees Fahrenheit. At this temperature another atomic reaction begins. Three helium atoms unite to form one carbon atom.

The star now has two sources of energy—first, the conversion of hydrogen into helium in the shell around the core and, second, the conversion of helium into carbon in the core.

What happens from this point on is not known with certainty. According to one theory, the star begins to grow hotter, and its color goes through a series of changes. The red giant becomes in turn an orange giant, a yellow giant, a white giant, and a blue giant.

The final chapters in a star's history depend upon how massive it was to begin with. If it was only a little more massive than the sun, it is now near the end of its career. It has now just about exhausted all of its atomic fuel.

Soon it can generate heat and light only by further contraction. The star is now shrinking rapidly and on its way to becoming a white dwarf.

The star is now dying, but apparently it does not always give up easily. It may become a nova, perhaps a repeating nova, blowing off shells of gas in one or more terrific explosions.

Finally, it becomes a white dwarf, perhaps no larger than the moon. It is now so tightly compressed that a spoonful of its material weighs several tons. It no longer has any source of heat and light. It is cooling off and some day will be just a cold, dead sphere.

Highly luminous stars, which are comparatively rare, have a different life history. One of these stars continues to produce energy even after it has converted much of the helium in its core into carbon. It develops three zones of energy production. In addition to producing helium from hydrogen and carbon from helium, it begins to convert the carbon at the center of the core into heavier elements.

In this way, scientists now believe, the heavier chemical elements are created in the interior of stars.

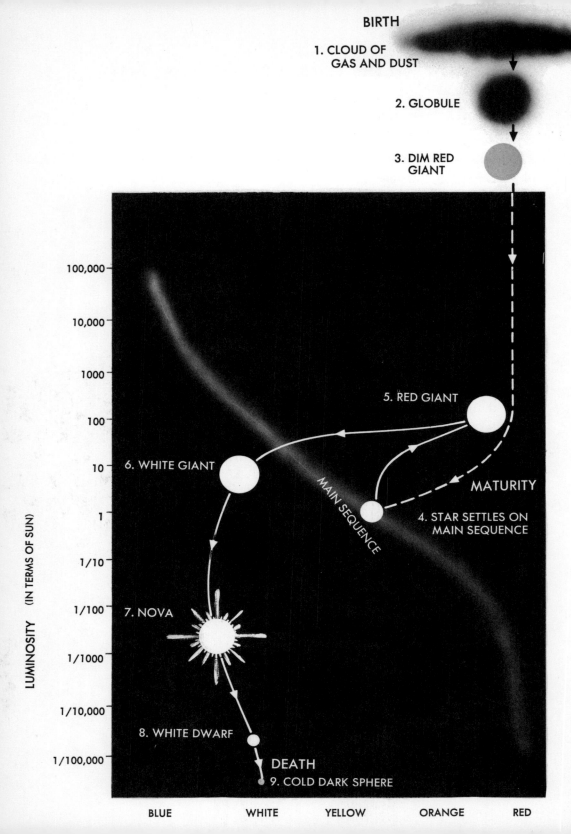

BIRTH

1. CLOUD OF
GAS AND DUST

2. GLOBULE

3. DIM RED
GIANT

100,000

10,000

1000

100   5. RED GIANT

10

6. WHITE GIANT

MAIN SEQUENCE

1   MATURITY

4. STAR SETTLES ON
MAIN SEQUENCE

1/10

1/100   7. NOVA

1/1000

1/10,000

8. WHITE DWARF

1/100,000   DEATH

9. COLD DARK SPHERE

LUMINOSITY (IN TERMS OF SUN)

BLUE   WHITE   YELLOW   ORANGE   RED

But because of the tremendous temperatures involved, the giant star may become extremely unstable during the closing chapters of its life. If it explodes, it becomes a supernova, a million times more luminous than it was originally. But after the explosion, it is only a dwarf white star surrounded by a complex tangle of gaseous clouds and filaments. It, too, will grow dimmer with the passage of time and finally go out.

The life history of a star, similar to our sun, plotted on the H-R diagram. This chart does not show motions of the star in the heavens, but its changes in color, luminosity, and size from birth to death. The evolutionary track of a more massive star would lie higher in the diagram, that of a less massive star lower. The more massive a star is, the faster it evolves.

69

12

The distances of
the stars

It is a simple matter to measure the distance from the door of a house to a tree on the front lawn. But how would you measure the distance to a tree on the opposite bank of a swiftly flowing river? A surveyor has a clever way of doing this.

He measures off a base line along the bank of the river. Let us say it is 1,000 feet long. Then he sights at the tree from either end of his base line, noting in each case the angle which his little telescope makes with the base line.

He now has a triangle of which he knows the length of the base and the angles which the other two sides make with it.

He can now find the distance to the tree by drawing the triangle to scale, letting an inch, for example, represent 100 feet. A simpler method is to calculate the distance with the aid of *trigonometry*, the branch of mathematics which deals with the relationships between the sides and angles of triangles.

The surveyor's trick is known as *triangulation*. The astronomer uses it to measure distances in the solar system and to the stars. But he encounters many difficulties because his base line is always so much shorter than the distances he is trying to measure.

Instead of measuring the angles at the base of the triangle, he

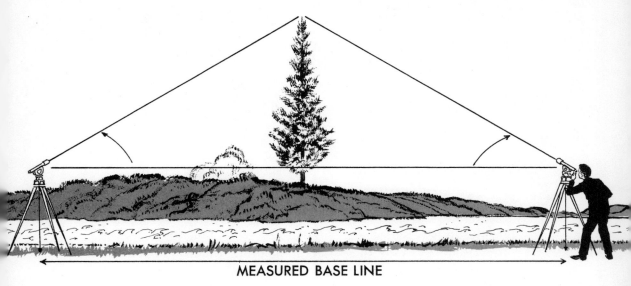

MEASURED BASE LINE

A surveyor calculates the distance to a tree across the river by measuring a base line, and then finding the angles from each end of the line to the tree.

determines the angle at the apex of the triangle.

A simple experiment will show you how this can be done. Hold a pencil upright at arm's length. Close your left eye and with your right eye note the position of the pencil against the background of the opposite wall of the room. Now open your left eye and close your right eye. The pencil appears to shift its position against the background. The apparent shift is due to the fact that you are now looking at the pencil from a different angle.

From the shift, it is possible to calculate the angle which the pencil makes with the base line, which in this experiment is the distance between your two eyes. This apparent shift of an object as seen from two different points is known as *parallax*.

This method is used to find the distance to the moon. Two

observatories, thousands of miles apart, photograph the moon at the same time. The photographs show a shift in the moon's position against the background of stars. It is now possible to calculate the angle which the moon makes with the two observatories. This is the apex of a triangle which has the distance between the observatories for a base.

Using the same method, astronomers determined the distance to Eros, one of the asteroids which occasionally comes close to the earth. Since the relative distance of bodies in the solar system can be determined from their motions, it was then possible to calculate other distances in the solar system, including the distance from the earth to the sun.

The stars are so very far away that the distance between two observatories is not enough for a base line to determine the distance of even the nearest star. But once the distance to the sun was known, a new base line was available. It was the diameter of the earth's yearly orbit around the sun. Two photographs were taken of a star six months apart. The shift of the star's position against the background of faint stars was then measured.

The mile is much too short a yardstick for convenience when we are talking about the distances of the stars. Astronomers find it easier to use the unit of measurement known as the *light-year*. It is about six trillion miles, the distance which light, going 186,000 miles a second, covers in one year.

Astronomers use triangulation in determining the distance to the moon or a nearby planet (left). The base line is the distance between two observatories. In finding the distance to a far-off star (right), the baseline is the diameter of the earth's orbit around the sun.

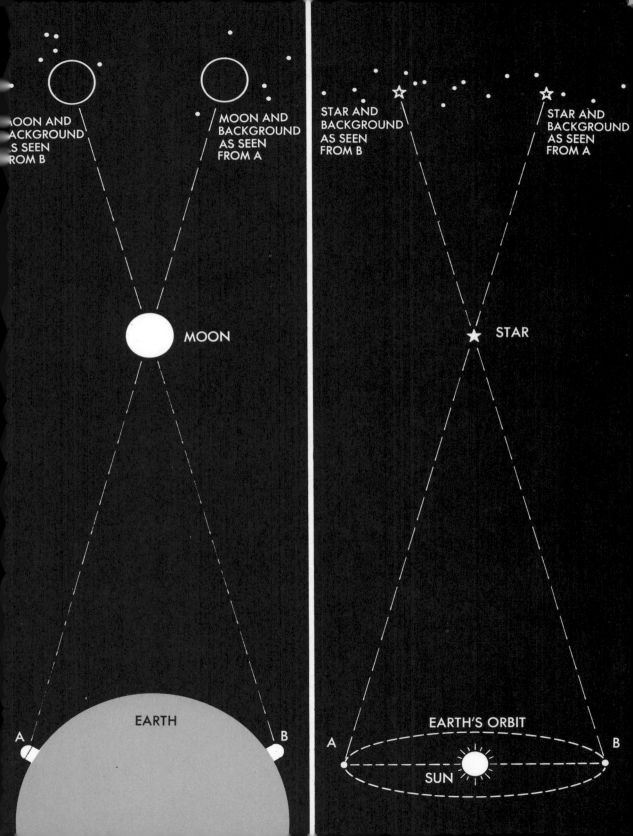

MOON AND BACKGROUND AS SEEN FROM B

MOON AND BACKGROUND AS SEEN FROM A

MOON

EARTH

A

B

STAR AND BACKGROUND AS SEEN FROM B

STAR AND BACKGROUND AS SEEN FROM A

STAR

EARTH'S ORBIT

A

B

SUN

Astronomers have succeeded in determining the distances of about 6,000 of the nearer stars by the method of parallax. The most distant stars charted in this fashion are about 300 light-years away.

Once the distance of a star is known, it is possible to calculate its actual brightness or luminosity from its apparent brightness or magnitude.

It is not possible to determine directly the distances of stars more than 300 light-years away. The parallax is so small that it cannot be measured. Indirect methods must be used.

By noting the color and spectrum of a distant star, we can determine its location on the H-R diagram. This tells us its luminosity. We can then calculate its distance by comparing its apparent magnitude with its luminosity. Giant and supergiant stars are used for this purpose since they are the most luminous stars and consequently can be seen at the greatest distances.

Among the most useful stars for estimating great distances are the variable stars known as the Cepheids. (You met them in Chapter 8.) It has been found that there is a direct relationship between the period of a Cepheid and its actual brightness or luminosity. (By *period*, the astronomer here means the time it takes the star to go from minimum brightness to maximum and back to minimum.) Consequently, once we measure the period of a Cepheid, we know its luminosity. Its distance can then be calculated from its apparent magnitude.

Alpha Centauri, the nearest star, is a little over four light-years away. Sirius, the Dog Star, is almost nine light-years away. Fifteen stars are known to be within 12 light-years of the earth. All the others are farther away. Some are 100 light-years away, still others

1,000, or 10,000—or almost 100,000 light-years.

Think what this means. These figures not only tell us how far away a star is, but how long it takes its light, traveling 186,000 miles a second, to reach the earth.

When you go outdoors on a clear night, the particular beam of light which reaches your eye from some star may have started toward you the year you were born. The beam of light from another star may have started toward you just about the time George Washington was crossing the Delaware. The light that meets your eye from a third may have started toward you when much of North America was buried under glaciers in the Ice Age and prehistoric men were living in caves.

13

Our galaxy

The Milky Way is best seen in the country, away from the glare of city lights and neon signs, on a clear moonless night in late summer. Then it can be seen in its full glory, a luminous band of shining gold, stretching from horizon to horizon and passing high overhead.

The band is irregular in shape, and some parts are brighter than others. Starting at the constellation of Cygnus or the Northern Cross, high overhead in the summertime, the band toward the south is split in two by a dark streak. This streak is called the Great Rift.

In ancient times people had no idea what the Milky Way really was. The Greeks said it was a road leading to the home of the gods. The mystery was solved when Galileo turned his little telescope on the heavens in 1609. He found that the Milky Way consisted of thousands upon thousands of stars too faint to be seen individually with the unaided eye. Modern telescopes have revealed great patches of bright nebulae among the clouds of stars, as well as many dark nebulae. The largest of the dark nebulae is the Great Rift.

When a big telescope is turned on the Milky Way, it seems as

Harlow Shapley, who pioneered in establishing the true size of our galaxy and the location of our sun in it.

though the stars must be countless and that they stretch away to infinity. But astronomers know that this is not so. The stars thin out at great distances, forming a system which is limited in size and numbers. Our sun with its planets is part of this system. Often we speak of it as our galaxy or the Milky Way Galaxy because, as we shall see in the next chapter, it is only one of many such galaxies in the universe.

The first attempt to discover the shape of our galaxy was made in 1784 by a great British astronomer, Sir William Herschel. Counting the number of stars to be seen with his telescope in different parts of the sky, he noted that the number grew greater as the band of the Milky Way was approached.

From this he concluded that the stars were arranged in a great system shaped like a grindstone or a watch. The Milky Way as we see it in the heavens is the view which we get of this system from our position inside it.

When we look at the Milky Way, we see so great a concentration of stars because we are looking into the depths of the galaxy. We are looking along the hands of the watch, as it were. When we look away from the Milky Way, we see so few stars because we are looking out through the face of the watch.

Herschel thought that the sun was situated near the center of the galaxy. But in this he was wrong. The modern view of the structure of the galaxy had its beginnings in the studies of Harlow Shapley in 1916. Shapley showed that our sun was far from the center of the galaxy.

We know today that the galaxy is a great flattened system of about 100 billion stars and enough gas and dust to equal many more billions of stars. The system is about 100,000 light-years in diameter.

The center of the galaxy is in the great star clouds in the direction of the constellation of Sagittarius, which you can see low on the southern horizon in summer.

This central region of the galaxy is a vast assemblage of stars in the form of a flattened sphere. It has a diameter of about 20,000 light-years and is about 6,000 light-years from top to bottom. The stars in it are two or three times as close to each other on the average as the stars in the neighborhood of the sun.

We do not get as good a view of this central region as we would like because of the dark clouds of the Great Rift. Astronomers believe that its very center or nucleus consists of a still greater con-

This remarkable photograph, taken with a wide-angle lens from the Southern Hemisphere, reveals part of the disk-like structure of the Milky Way Galaxy. (The dark bars belong to the framework of the telescope.)

centration of stars. This nucleus, in which the stars are as crowded as in the globular clusters, is thought to be about 5,000 light-years in diameter.

Surrounding the central region, there is a great flat disk of stars with a diameter of about 100,000 light-years. In this flat disk of stars are spiral arms composed of more stars, gas, and dust. At least two arms emerge from the central region and coil around it.

In addition to the denser clouds of gas and dust in the spiral arms of the galaxy, there is an all-pervading haze of gas and dust that extends throughout the central plane of the galaxy.

Our solar system—the sun and its planets, including the earth—is located in one of the spiral arms toward the outer edge of the galaxy. We are about 27,000 light-years from the center of the galaxy.

As we saw in Chapter 10, there are two kinds of star clusters—galactic clusters and globular clusters. The galactic clusters occur in the spiral arms.

The globular clusters show quite a different distribution. They surround the galaxy on all sides, forming a spherical halo around it. Their distances from the center of the galaxy range from about 10,000 light-years to more than 50,000. This halo also contains a sprinkling of individual stars and a great cloud of gas.

One of the most interesting facts about the galaxy is that it is rotating. This vast assembly of 100 billion stars with its clouds of gas and dust is turning around its center. It is like a gigantic merry-go-round. Viewed from "above"—from the point which astronomers call the *north galactic pole*—the rotation is clockwise.

In Chapter 7, we saw that the sun is moving toward the constellation of Hercules with a velocity of 12 miles a second. This is the motion of the sun with relation to the stars in its neighborhood. But the sun and all of its neighboring stars are part of the great carrousel, going around the center of the galaxy with immense speed.

The rate of rotation is probably uniform in the central region of the galaxy, but it becomes less in the disk with increasing distance

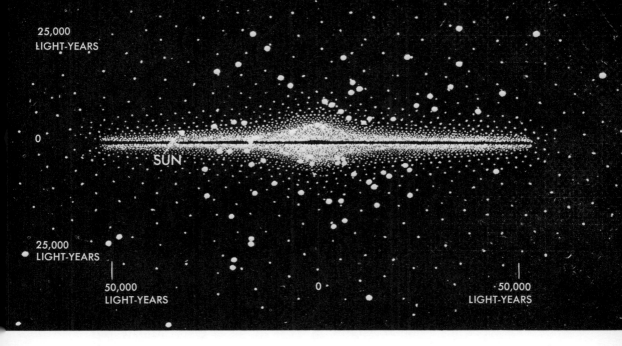

25,000
LIGHT-YEARS

0

SUN

25,000
LIGHT-YEARS

50,000
LIGHT-YEARS

0

50,000
LIGHT-YEARS

Viewed edge-on, our galaxy has a lens shape. The large dots represent the globular clusters in the halo around our galaxy. The small dots represent stars. Notice that our sun is not located in the center of the galaxy.

from the center. Our sun is going around the galactic center with the amazing velocity of 200 miles a second. But the galaxy is so huge that it takes the sun 250 million years to make one trip around the galaxy. If the sun is five billion years old, it has made only 20 trips around the galaxy since it was born.

This rotation, however, is not shared by the globular clusters and the stars in the galactic halo. The globular clusters are moving in vast elliptical orbits around the galactic center at all angles to the disk of the galaxy. The stars in the halo have similar motions.

What astronomers have learned about the structure of our galaxy is one of the great triumphs of twentieth-century astronomy.

81

14

The distant galaxies

The true grandeur of the universe has only been appreciated in the last forty years. We now know that our vast, magnificent galaxy is only one of many in the universe. The number is almost incredible. There are at least 100 billion galaxies within reach of the 200-inch telescope on Palomar Mountain. It is impossible to estimate the total number in the universe. It may be a million times a trillion. The number may even be *infinite*—that is, going on and on without end.

Viewed in a small telescope, the distant galaxies appear as small patches of light scattered among the stars. A bigger telescope will reveal that some of the nearer ones have a spiral structure resembling pinwheel fireworks. At the start of the twentieth century, astronomers were not yet certain whether these *spiral nebulae*, as they were then called, were inside our galaxy or beyond it. It is now known, as we saw in the previous chapter, that our own galaxy has such spiral arms.

Big telescopes had resolved the outer portions of some of the nearer ones into what looked like individual stars. But there was much discussion as to whether they really were stars. Some astronomers thought that the spiral nebulae were quite small, and that the starlike objects were merely knots of nebulous material.

The argument was settled in 1923, when Edwin P. Hubble, using the 100-inch telescope on Mt. Wilson, discovered a Cepheid variable star in the outer portion of the Andromeda Galaxy, then known as the Great Nebula in Andromeda. This not only proved that the starlike objects were really stars but made it possible to estimate the distance to the Great Nebula. It was now obvious that it was far beyond our own galaxy and was indeed a galaxy itself. In the next couple of years Hubble located several more Cepheids in the Andromeda Galaxy.

I made my first visit to Mt. Wilson in 1926. I still remember the thrill when Dr. Hubble showed me the photographic plate, taken with the 100-inch telescope, on which he had discovered that first Cepheid. It was truly one of the great milestones in the history of astronomy.

The biggest telescopes show considerable detail in the galaxies which are nearest to us. Less detail can be seen in the more distant ones. The most distant ones are only fuzzy spots even in the great 200-inch telescope on Palomar Mountain. But whereas the stars in our galaxy thin out with distance, thus showing the limits of the galaxy, there is no such thinning out in the numbers of the galaxies with distance. That is why astronomers think that there are many more beyond the range of the 200-inch telescope.

Most of the galaxies are smaller than our own, but some are undoubtedly larger. An average galaxy is believed to contain about 10 billion stars. Our own galaxy, you will recall, contains about 100 billion stars.

It is possible to divide the galaxies into three general types. These are the *spiral galaxies*, the *elliptical galaxies*, and the *irregular galaxies*.

About three-fourths of the known galaxies are spiral galaxies. Some have a large central region and thin, closely coiled arms. Others have smaller centers and more extended arms.

We see many spirals edgewise. These show clearly the bulge of the central region and the disk of stars extending from it. Most of these show a dark streak dividing the galaxy lengthwise. This con-

Left: A spiral galaxy seen full-face. Right: Another spiral galaxy seen edgewise. The Milky Way Galaxy, if seen from several millions of light-years away, would look very much like these galaxies.

sists of gas and dust in the plane of the galaxy.

A number of spiral galaxies are known as barred spiral galaxies. Their spiral arms emerge from a bright bar that extends across their center.

The elliptical galaxies resemble oversized globular clusters. Some are globular but others are more flattened.

A *barred spiral galaxy*

An *elliptical galaxy*

A smaller number of galaxies are the irregular galaxies. They are ragged collections of stars, lacking the orderly structure of the spiral and elliptical galaxies.

Present-day study of the distant galaxies is being carried on along two general lines. One is the study of the detailed structure of the galaxies which are closest to us. The other is the study of the distribution of the galaxies in space and their motions. Both studies are giving us new insight into the nature and structure of the universe.

15

The local group

The distant galaxies are scattered more or less uniformly throughout space. But here and there we find close pairs of galaxies, small groups, or even large clusters. Thousands of clusters of galaxies are known, containing from 50 to as many as 10,000 galaxies.

Our galaxy is a member of a cosmic club that includes 17 members. It is a group of galaxies to which astronomers have given the dull and unimaginative name of the Local Group. It consists of three spiral galaxies including our own, four irregular ones, and ten elliptical ones. Six of the elliptical galaxies are of low luminosity and are sometimes called *dwarf ellipticals*.

The Local Group occupies an egg-shaped volume of space with our own galaxy near one end and the Andromeda Galaxy at the other end. It is 2,200,000 light-years from our galaxy to the Andromeda Galaxy.

The Andromeda Galaxy is the nearest and brightest of the normal spiral galaxies. It is the only spiral galaxy that can be seen with the unaided eye.

It is easy to find the Andromeda Galaxy. Look first for the Great Square in Pegasus. This is a square of four bright stars, larger than the bowl of the Big Dipper. It comes over the eastern horizon in August, is best seen high in the southern sky during the autumn,

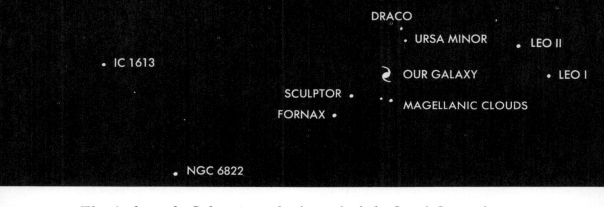

DRACO

· URSA MINOR   · LEO II

· IC 1613

OUR GALAXY   · LEO I

SCULPTOR ·

FORNAX ·   MAGELLANIC CLOUDS

· NGC 6822

The Andromeda Galaxy is at the far end of the Local Group from our own Milky Way Galaxy—more than two million light-years distant (above). But you can see the Andromeda Galaxy on a clear night if you look near the Great Square of Pegasus (below).

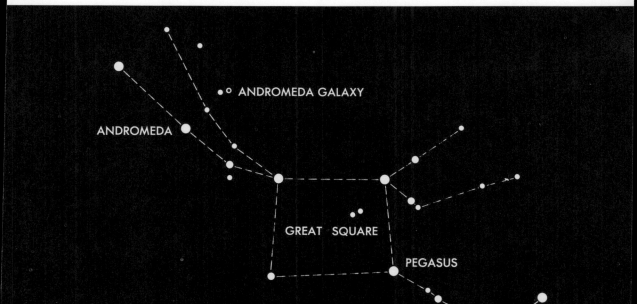

ANDROMEDA GALAXY

ANDROMEDA

GREAT   SQUARE

PEGASUS

and disappears below the western horizon in February.

Actually only three of the stars belong to the constellation of Pegasus, the winged horse. The star in the northeast corner of the square belongs to the constellation of Andromeda, which stretches upward and to the east. If you look a little to the east of this star and a little higher in the sky, you will note what appears to be a fuzzy star. That tiny spot is the Andromeda Galaxy.

A small telescope will make the spot appear larger and will show that it has an oval shape. But it will tell you nothing about the real nature of the spot. Our present knowledge of the Andromeda Galaxy was made possible mostly by the giant telescopes on Mt. Wilson and Palomar Mountain.

The distance of the Andromeda Galaxy has been determined from observation of the Cepheid variable stars in it. Once the distance was determined, it was possible to calculate the size of the Andromeda Galaxy. It has a diameter of 120,000 light-years.

This means that the Andromeda Galaxy is larger than our own galaxy. Previously, it had seemed that our galaxy was the largest in the universe. Astronomers remembered that people had once thought the earth was the center of the universe; then people thought the sun was at the center of the galaxy. Each of these notions turned out to be wrong. Astronomers could think of no reason why our galaxy should be the largest in the universe. So they were relieved to find out that the Andromeda Galaxy is larger.

The structure of the Andromeda Galaxy is very much like that of our own. There is the same central region surrounded by a flattened disk. At the heart of the central bulge there is a very bright

The Andromeda Galaxy

90

nucleus, undoubtedly a dense concentration of stars resembling a giant globular cluster. Two or more spiral arms, coming from the central region, are located in the disk.

Surrounding the Andromeda Galaxy there is a halo of globular clusters. About 250 have been counted.

The two members of the Local Group closest to our own are both irregular galaxies. In fact, they are so close, as distances go in the universe, that astronomers regard them as satellites of our galaxy. They are the Large and Small Magellanic Clouds.

The Magellanic Clouds were first noticed by the Portuguese explorers of the sixteenth century as their ships approached the Cape of Good Hope. They called them "Cape Clouds." Subsequently, astronomers named them in honor of the explorer who first sailed around the earth.

Situated not far from the south pole of the heavens, they cannot be seen from northern latitudes. To the unaided eye, they look like pieces of the Milky Way that have broken loose.

The two are about 150,000 light-years away. The Large Magellanic Cloud is about 30,000 light-years in diameter, the Small Magellanic Cloud about 20,000.

The Large Magellanic Cloud, though smaller than our own galaxy, is larger and brighter than the average galaxy. It contains many highly luminous stars. Its brightest stars are blue supergiants. The brightest star known to astronomers is in the Large Magellanic Cloud. Known as S Doradus, it is a million times more luminous than our own sun. There are many Cepheid variables in the cloud.

The Large Magellanic Cloud also contains many clusters of stars like our own galactic clusters. Some are embedded in gaseous

The Large and Small Magellanic Clouds are thought to be satellites of our galaxy. The bright star at the upper right is Achernar, a star in our own galaxy.

nebulae like the Pleiades. The Cloud contains many diffuse nebulae like the Great Nebula in Orion. The largest is known as the Loop Nebula.

The Cloud is undoubtedly full of gas and dust. The dust is so thick that is is impossible to see more distant galaxies through the Cloud.

The Small Magellanic Cloud is likewise rich in blue supergiants. However, it contains less dust so that more distant galaxies can be seen through it.

The Local Group is held together by the gravitational attraction of the galaxies in it. Just as our own galaxy is rotating, it is possible that the Local Group is rotating around a common center of gravity. However, this is not yet known with certainty.

16

The evolution of galaxies

Studying the distant galaxies which he had photographed with the 100-inch telescope on Mt. Wilson, Hubble saw that he could arrange them in an orderly sequence on the basis of their shapes. The sequence began with the elliptical galaxies which were spherical in form. It proceeded through the more flattened forms to those that were most flattened. Then it split into two branches, one consisting of the normal spirals, the other of the barred spirals. In each branch the sequence proceeded from those with tightly coiled spiral arms to those with wide open arms. The Hubble sequence is shown in the diagram.

At one time astronomers were inclined to think that this sequence represented the way in which galaxies developed. It was thought that the elliptical galaxies were young galaxies and the spiral galaxies old ones. Astronomers today doubt that one type of galaxy can evolve into another. There are important differences in the composition of the different types of galaxies.

The irregular galaxies abound in highly luminous blue stars embedded in glowing clouds of gas. These are young stars.

In the spiral galaxies, highly luminous blue stars are found only amid the gas and dust of the spiral arms. The central region and its surrounding disk consist largely of red dwarf stars. The brightest

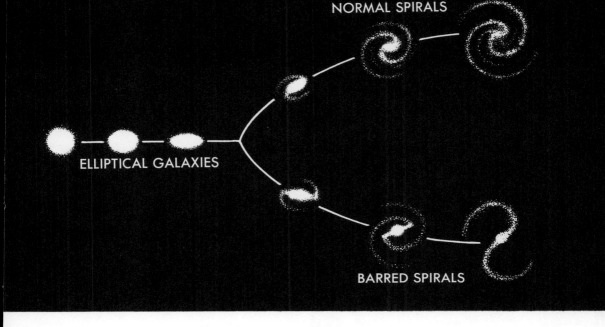

NORMAL SPIRALS

ELLIPTICAL GALAXIES

BARRED SPIRALS

The Hubble sequence

stars in the central region are red giants. These are old stars, billions of years old.

This difference between the central region and the spiral arms was first pointed out by Walter Baade of the Mt. Wilson and Palomar Observatories from a detailed study of the Andromeda Galaxy. He called the young stars of the spiral arms Population I stars; those of the central region, Population II stars.

The elliptical galaxies contain almost no gas or dust and no young stars. They consist of Population II stars.

Many astronomers today tend to believe that each type of galaxy has its own pattern and rate of evolution. You will recall from Chapter 11 that this is the case with individual stars. A highly luminous blue star has a pattern that differs from that of a yellow or red dwarf.

It is supposed that, at a very early stage, the universe consisted

of an extremely thin cloud or fog of hydrogen gas that filled all space. Random motions of the hydrogen atoms caused denser spots to form in it. Gravitation caused these spots to become centers which attracted more gas to themselves. As a result, the fog broke up into a vast number of separate, swirling clouds. These were *proto-galaxies*. The future development of each proto-galaxy depended upon its mass and its rate of rotation.

If the proto-galaxy was very massive and rotating slowly, it contracted into a sphere. If it was less massive and rotating more rapidly, it assumed a more flattened shape. In time stars formed. The proto-galaxy became an elliptical galaxy.

The first stars to form in a galaxy would be large, very hot, highly luminous blue stars. You will recall from Chapter 11 that these form most rapidly. But they would burn up their nuclear fuel in 10 or 20 million years, ending their lives as white dwarfs. However, before the end, they would become supernovae returning great amounts of gaseous material to the galaxy. This material would contain helium and heavier chemical elements that had formed in these stars. As a result, the composition of the gaseous clouds in the galaxy would be changed by the addition of these other chemical elements. These heavier elements would form dust grains and in time there would be a small percentage of dust in the gaseous clouds.

Meanwhile, the formation of stars would continue in the galaxy.

Walter Baade, using the "blink microscope" to locate variable stars in photographs of the Milky Way. The instrument compares two pictures of one area taken at different times, in order to detect a change of brightness in a star.

More short-lived blue stars would form, but yellow and red dwarfs would also begin to take shape. These smaller stars burn their nuclear fuel slowly and remain unchanged for billions of years. Eventually all the gas and dust of the galaxy would be used up in the creation of these long-lived stars. There would be none left to form new stars. And so the elliptical galaxy would consist only of old stars.

It is thought that a proto-galaxy less massive than an elliptical galaxy and rotating very rapidly would evolve into a spiral galaxy. Stars would evolve first in the dense center of the proto-galaxy and this would become the central region of the spiral galaxy. Because of the rapid rotation, the rest of the proto-galaxy would be spun out into a flat disk around the central region.

The gas would be drawn into spiral arms, and stars would form in these arms. The first spiral arms would be disrupted by the continued rotation, but new ones would form. In time the central region of the galaxy would be surrounded by a great disk of stars in which there were spiral arms of gas and dust with new stars still forming in these newest spiral arms.

Most of the irregular galaxies are small. Frequently they are found near spiral galaxies. It has been suggested that they were formed from gas and dust that had been ejected from spiral galaxies. This would explain why they were so much younger than the spiral and elliptical galaxies.

Astronomers do not yet have enough information to construct a completely satisfactory theory of the evolution of galaxies. Perhaps in another few years it will be possible to do so.

17

Radio astronomy

The newest branch of astronomy is known as radio astronomy. It was born in 1931 when a young American radio engineer, Karl Jansky, discovered that radio waves were reaching the earth from the center of the Milky Way. The waves made a hissing noise in the earphones of his radio equipment.

At the time, Jansky was attempting to discover the source of radio noises that were interfering with transatlantic radio reception. He was using a directional antenna which indicated the direction from which radio signals came.

The radio telescope is basically such a directional radio antenna connected to a very sensitive radio receiving set. The waves are made visible on an instrument called an *oscillograph*. They are also recorded on tape.

Radio telescopes differ widely in appearance depending upon the design of the antenna system. Some look like exaggerated versions of the television antenna on the roof of a house. Others resemble the radar equipment that came into use during World War II. Still others are huge complexes of steel masts and wire nets. Many radio telescopes employ an array of small antennas mounted on some sort of framework. The most spectacular ones have great steel or aluminum bowls that can be pointed at any part of the sky.

Three modern radio telescopes. Top: A mile-long antenna at Mills Cross near Canberra, Australia. Right: The 250-foot "dish" at Jodrell Bank, England, the world's largest fully steerable radio telescope. Bottom: A vast radio telescope built in a natural hollow of the earth at Arecibo, Puerto Rico.

The world's largest radio telescope that can be pointed at any spot in the sky is in England, not far from the city of Manchester, at a place called Jodrell Bank. I was invited to see the giant instrument just as the finishing touches were put on it in 1957.

Motoring from Manchester to Jodrell Bank, my attention was suddenly arrested by a fantastic sight. We were driving in a drizzling rain, and the rolling hills were a soft gray in the half-fog that filled the air. Suddenly out of the mists there arose a vast structure of weird shape, towering to ten times the height of the trees, but seemingly made of gossamer threads. It appeared to be a gigantic bowl hung between two slim towers of lace.

A few hours later, closer inspection verified that this lacy structure is built of solid steel girders. The twin towers are 185 feet high, and the bowl hung between them is 250 feet in diameter.

In company with the engineer in charge, I took the elevator to the top of one of the towers. Then in the drizzling rain, we went out on the narrow catwalk that leads to the center of the great steel bowl. Only here is it possible to appreciate the mammoth size of the structure.

The steel towers are not planted firmly in the ground but are mounted on wheels on a circular railway track so that the whole structure can be turned around in a circle.

Radio waves reach the earth from the sun and from about 2,000 distinct spots in the heavens. These spots have become known as *radio stars*, although it was quickly realized that they must be much larger than individual stars. So far, astronomers have succeeded in identifying about 100 of them with objects that can be seen with large optical telescopes.

The first radio star to be identified proved to be the Crab Nebula in the constellation of Taurus. As we saw in Chapter 8, the tangled filaments of this nebula are the remnants of the supernova that appeared in 1054.

Another radio star is the spot where Tycho's Nova appeared in 1572. Not even the 200-inch telescope can find any visible trace of it. But it seems as though the ghost of Tycho's Nova haunts the sky. More puzzling is the fact that, while optical telescopes disclose the remnants of Kepler's Nova, the supernova of 1604, no radio waves have been detected from it.

One intense radio star is in the constellation of Cassiopeia, the familiar "W" of stars not far from the North Star.

Radio astronomers named this radio star Cassiopeia A, but

The constellation of Cassiopeia

they refer to it as "Cass" for short. Once its exact location had been pinpointed, the astronomers on Palomar Mountain turned the 200-inch telescope on it. Photographs taken with the giant telescope revealed a curving arc of luminous gases millions of miles long. Below it there was a hodgepodge of streaks and filaments and broken bits of nebulous material. They occupied a region of space calculated to have a volume of 15,000 cubic light-years. The whole region is one of incredible motion and turbulence. Some of the filaments are swirling about with speeds of 3,000 miles per second. Other radio stars have been identified with similar chaotic areas.

Not all the radio stars lie within our own galaxy. Radio waves have been detected from some of the nearer galaxies, including the Andromeda Galaxy. This was expected, once sufficiently large and sensitive radio telescopes were available.

More amazing was the discovery that some radio stars were situated in the far reaches of the universe, far beyond the galaxies of the Local Group. These have turned out to be the most exciting objects known to astronomers. The first one identified was in the constellation of Cygnus, the Swan.

The 200-inch telescope shows that the radio star in Cygnus looks like two galaxies crashing face to face, like a pair of cymbals banged together by the drummer of a symphony orchestra. If this is indeed the case, it is a cosmic traffic accident of incredible size. However, some astronomers think that this radio star is really one galaxy that has split in half.

Recent studies with the most powerful radio telescopes have disclosed that the radio waves do not originate in the visible components of the radio star, but in invisible clouds on either side of it. It is thought that these are clouds of electrons trapped in mag-

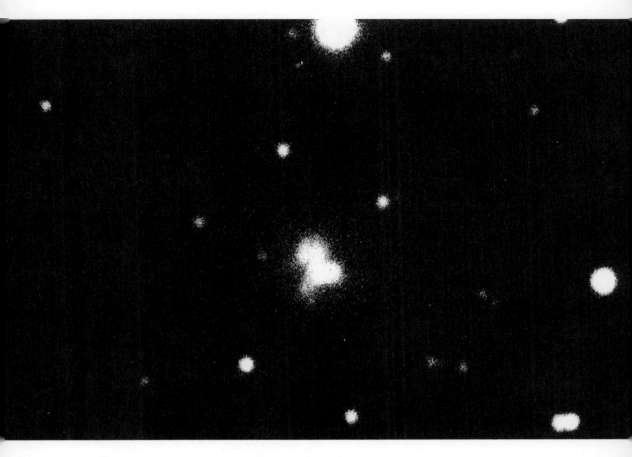

This source of radio noise in Cygnus is thought by some astronomers to be an exploding galaxy—by others to be two colliding galaxies.

netic fields.

A number of other radio stars have been found to resemble the one in Cygnus.

In 1963 astronomers found that strong radio waves were coming from objects that had been previously regarded as faint bluish stars in our galaxy. Further study revealed that they were not in our galaxy but at immense distances from it. Astronomers call them *quasi-stellar* radio sources—or *quasars* for short.

About 50 of them have been found, and some of them appear to be the most distant known objects in the universe—billions of light years away. It appears that they are the biggest, most luminous, and most massive objects in the universe. It is probable that one is as big as a billion stars.

The radio waves tuned in by radio telescopes range from very short waves, whose wave length is about a tenth of an inch, to waves about 90 feet long. However, special significance attaches to one particular wave length. This is 8.4 inches—21 centimeters on the metric scale.

The 21-centimeter waves originate in clouds of hydrogen which lie in the spiral arms of our galaxy. With optical telescopes, it is possible to see such clouds only when they have been made phosphorescent by the radiations of very hot stars, or when the clouds reflect the light of nearby stars. These luminous clouds, as we saw in Chapter 9, are the diffuse nebulae.

The way in which these 21-centimeter waves arise is quite interesting. A hydrogen atom has a nucleus consisting of one proton. One electron revolves around it. Both particles are spinning like tops in the same direction. But sometimes the electron flips over so that it is spinning in the opposite direction. When this happens, a radio wave is emitted.

You will remember that the hydrogen gas is largely concentrated in the spiral arms of our galaxy. Consequently astronomers have been able to map the spiral arms of our galaxy more clearly by mapping the areas in which the 21-centimeter waves are strongest.

In this way radio astronomy is extending our knowledge of the structure of our galaxy.

Astronomers are certain that radio astronomy will solve many of the mysteries surrounding the structure of our own galaxy and the evolution of the distant galaxies.

18

The expanding universe

The most amazing and exciting discovery in the history of modern astronomy was announced by Hubble at the Mt. Wilson Observatory in the year 1929.

As you will recall from Chapter 3, the motion of a star in the line of sight is revealed by its spectrum. If the star is moving toward the earth, the spectrum lines are shifted toward the violet end of the spectrum. If the star is moving away from us, the lines are shifted toward the red end.

The same thing is true of a distant galaxy. The spectrum of a galaxy is the combined spectrum of all the stars in it. As a result, the lines in the spectrum are somewhat fuzzy, but the prominent ones are easily identified and there is no difficulty about measuring their position.

In 1929 Hubble announced the results of a study he had made of the spectra of some 20 galaxies whose distances he had also determined. The most distant one was 20 million light-years away. He found that in every case the spectrum lines were shifted to the red, and that there was a direct relation between the amount of red shift and the distance of a galaxy. The farther away a galaxy was, the greater was the red shift. This meant that the galaxies were receding from the earth. And the farther away they were, the faster

Edwin P. Hubble, examining a photographic plate of a distant galaxy. His pioneering studies revealed the true nature of these galaxies and showed that the universe is expanding.

they were moving.

The speeds with which the galaxies were moving seemed incredible, but Hubble boldly predicted that the same relation would be found true for more distant galaxies. This relation between the distance of a galaxy and its speed became known as Hubble's law.

His prediction was verified by another astronomer at Mt. Wilson, Milton S. Humason, who undertook the laborious task of determining the red shift of more distant galaxies. By 1936, Humason had succeeded in measuring the speed of galaxies more than a billion

RELATION BETWEEN RED-SHIFT AND DISTANCE

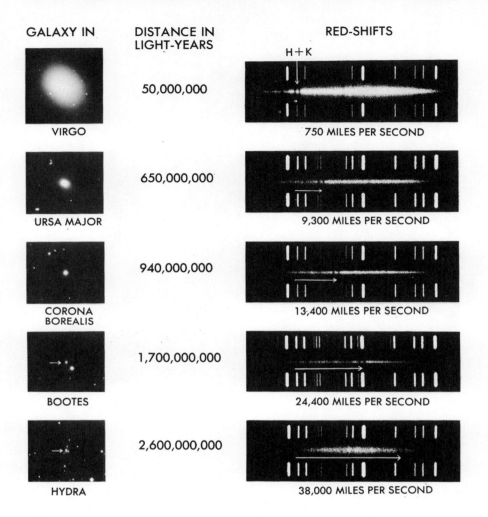

GALAXY IN	DISTANCE IN LIGHT-YEARS	RED-SHIFTS
VIRGO	50,000,000	H + K / 750 MILES PER SECOND
URSA MAJOR	650,000,000	9,300 MILES PER SECOND
CORONA BOREALIS	940,000,000	13,400 MILES PER SECOND
BOOTES	1,700,000,000	24,400 MILES PER SECOND
HYDRA	2,600,000,000	38,000 MILES PER SECOND

The speeds of distant galaxies, as revealed by the "red shift."

At the left are photographs of five galaxies, with their distances from the earth. At the right are their spectra. For comparison, a spectrum produced in the laboratory is shown above and below the spectrum of each galaxy.

The arrows call attention in each case to the shift of two prominent lines, known as the H and K lines, toward the red end of the spectrum. The speeds shown were calculated from these shifts.

110

light-years away. He found these galaxies receding with a speed of 24,000 miles per second.

Construction of the 200-inch telescope on Palomar Mountain enabled Humason and his colleagues to study still more distant galaxies. By 1956 they had measured the red shift of several hundred individual galaxies and 26 clusters of galaxies. The most distant ones, about 2½ billion light-years away, showed a velocity of 38,000 miles per second. This incredible velocity is one-fifth the speed of light. Since then, more distant galaxies have been found with velocities equal to one-half the speed of light.

Now, at first glance, it might seem as though our earth—or more exactly, our own galaxy—is some sort of center of repulsion from which all the other galaxies are running away. The farther away a galaxy is, the faster it is running away. But no explanation could be given for a such a state of affairs.

Hubble gave the correct explanation in 1929. The universe is expanding. If you were located on a planet circling a star in any galaxy in the universe, you would observe the same state of affairs. Every galaxy would appear to be running away from you. And the farther away a galaxy was, the faster it would be running away.

The idea of an expanding universe is startling. It is also difficult to grasp. Some scientists have attempted to find other explanations for the red shift. It has been suggested that the vibrations of the light rays from distant galaxies gradually slow up. But no basis can be found for this notion of "tired light."

A simple analogy, or comparison, will help you to picture the expanding universe. Suppose that you have pasted a large number of small paper dots on the surface of a rubber balloon. Now, if you blow more air into the balloon, the balloon will grow larger and its surface will expand. The distance between any two dots will grow greater. The greater the distance between any two dots to start with, the greater will be the rate at which the distance between them increases as the balloon expands.

In this analogy, you have used the surface of the balloon to represent the universe. The dots represent the galaxies.

In the universe, expansion does not take place within a galaxy or even within a group or cluster of galaxies. The galaxies within the Local Group do not obey Hubble's law. Within a galaxy or within a cluster of galaxies, gravitation holds the galaxy or the cluster together.

But the distances between galaxies and clusters of galaxies are constantly growing greater. It seems, therefore, as though it is space itself that is expanding. This is a startling idea, but most astronomers are inclined to accept it today.

So far in this book, we have been talking about objects in space. We must now turn our attention to space itself. We shall see that astronomers now think that space may be curved as well as expanding.

19

Curved space

The idea of *curved space* was suggested more than a century ago by a young German mathematician, Bernhard Riemann, in the year 1854. But it interested only a small number of mathematicians until Albert Einstein introduced it into his theory of relativity in 1915.

If space is curved, it must be curved into a fourth dimension. This is a puzzling idea since it is impossible to picture more than three dimensions of space. However, a simple analogy will help you to understand what is meant by the curvature of space.

The surface of the earth, like all surfaces, has two dimensions. But since it is the surface of a sphere, it is curved into the third dimension. It is *finite*, consisting of just so many square miles. But it is also *unbounded*: you can start anywhere on it and travel in any direction. But if you travel long enough in a straight line, you will find yourself back where you started.

Mathematicians call a surface like that of the earth a *closed surface* and speak of its curvature as *positive*.

There is another type of curvature like the surface of a saddle. This is called *negative curvature*. It is *open*. It does not close on itself like the surface of a sphere.

Mathematicians also use the term *zero curvature* to describe a plane surface, such as a table top, which has no curvature at all into the third dimension.

Einstein concluded that space has a positive curvature. This would mean that the universe is finite, though unbounded. If you started anywhere in the universe and traveled in what you supposed was a straight line, you would finally get back to the point where you started. (Of course, your journey would be one of many billions of light-years.)

Albert Einstein was only 26 years old, and living in Switzerland, when he published his special theory of relativity. This photograph shows Einstein in his study in Princeton, New Jersey, many years later.

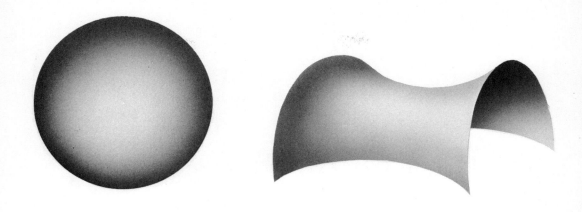

The surface of a sphere (left) has positive curvature. The surface of a saddle (right) has negative curvature.

In the 1920's three scientists, independently of each other, pointed out some consequences of the theory of relativity. The three were a Russian mathematician, Alexander Friedman, a Belgian mathematician, Abbé Georges Lemaître, and an American physicist, Howard P. Robertson. They showed that space may have positive, zero, or negative curvature. If space has positive curvature, it is closed and finite, as Einstein had imagined. But if it has zero or negative curvature, it is open and infinite.

However, the most startling conclusion which they drew from the theory of relativity was that the universe is unstable. It cannot be static. It must either expand or contract. There is no way to tell from the theory of relativity which it is doing.

But in 1929, as I related in the preceding chapter, Hubble discovered that the universe is expanding.

It is an astounding fact that this expansion was predicted from the theory of relativity before it was discovered by actual observation.

20

The big-bang theory

The fact that the universe is expanding led Lemaître to formulate an exciting theory of how the universe began.

The galaxies are rushing away from each other. Every day, the distance between galaxies and clusters of galaxies grows greater and greater. But what about the past? The galaxies were closer together yesterday. Longer ago they were even closer.

A simple analogy will help you picture this theory. Let us imagine that we have a motion picture of a crowd leaving a stadium after a football game. The film will show the people streaming out of the gate and scattering in all directions. Now, suppose we run the film backward. We will see the people backing up until they are all funneled back into the stadium gate.

Lemaître realized that if you went back far enough in time you would finally find space so contracted that all the galaxies were crowded together into one mass. He concluded that the universe began in just that way.

According to Lemaître, the whole universe was originally about the size of the planet Mars, a sphere about 4,000 miles in diameter. All the matter that we now find in the stars and nebulae of our galaxy and the other billions of galaxies was crowded into that space.

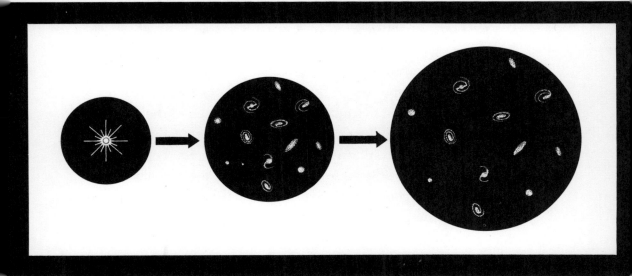

The Big-Bang Universe. According to this theory, the universe began with a great explosion. The galaxies thus formed are drawing farther and farther apart as space expands.

Lemaître called this original sphere of matter the *primeval atom.* Despite its size, the name is not unreasonable, because individual atoms did not exist within it. The subatomic particles which compose the atoms as we know them today were so crowded together that the great sphere formed one giant atom. A cubic inch of the primeval atom weighed about two billion tons.

Then the primeval atom exploded. That was the beginning of the universe. As the subatomic particles flew out in all directions, space began to expand.

Lemaître's theory was called the *exploding universe,* but astronomers today, with a pleasant show of humor, usually refer to it as the *big-bang theory*. In its present form it is largely the work of a Russian-born American scientist, George Gamow.

Gamow calculates that, at the moment of the explosion, the temperature of the primeval atom was about 25 billion degrees Fahrenheit. However, the temperature fell rapidly as space expanded. At the end of the first five minutes, the temperature of the universe dropped to about a billion degrees, and at the end of the first 250 million years it was down to about 200 degrees below zero.

At the moment of the explosion, the universe was a mighty blaze of light. But as it cooled it became dimmer until the whole universe was in utter darkness. It remained dark until the cosmic cloud broke up into proto-galaxies and stars took form within them.

It is interesting to picture what a dramatic moment that must have been, many billions of years ago, when the first star began to shine in one of the proto-galaxies. At that moment, light returned to the universe. Soon after, as time is measured in astronomy, the galaxies were glowing with billions of stars and the universe had acquired the majesty and beauty which greet our eyes today.

21

The steady-state theory

A theory about the nature of the universe that is completely different from the big-bang theory has been advanced by three British astronomers, Fred Hoyle, Herman Bondi, and Thomas Gold. It has been named the *steady-state theory*.

According to this theory the large-scale features of the universe do not change with time. The universe has always been essentially as it is today, and always will be. The universe had no beginning and it will have no end. Both space and time are infinite.

The advocates of the steady-state theory agree that the universe is expanding. They accept the red shifts in the spectra of the distant galaxies as proof of this.

But if space is expanding and the galaxies are spreading apart, it would appear that space is growing more and more empty with the passage of time. The number of galaxies in a given volume of space must decrease as time goes on. It would seem, therefore, that large-scale changes must occur in the universe with the passage of time.

The steady-state theory answers this difficulty by assuming that, as the galaxies draw apart, new galaxies come into existence in the space between them. The rate at which these new galaxies form is just enough to balance the spread of the old galaxies. Consequently, while the universe changes in detail, it remains basically

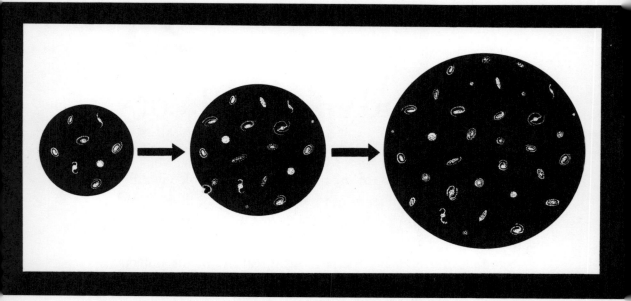

The Steady-State Universe. In this theory, the universe has no be-ginning and no end. As space expands and the galaxies draw apart, new ones are formed between them.

the same.

The theory holds that hydrogen atoms are created in space and that in time these atoms form great clouds which evolve into gal-axies. Because of this constant appearance of hydrogen atoms, the steady-state theory is also called the *theory of continuous creation.*

Hoyle estimates that one atom a year is created in a volume of space equal to that of a skyscraper. This does not seem like a lot of hydrogen until you remember that it is going on everywhere in space, and that space is very large. The rate suggested by Hoyle would mean the creation of trillions of hydrogen atoms every second in each cubic light-year of space.

If this is the case, an extremely thin cloud of hydrogen, gradually growing thicker, must exist in space between the galaxies. With the passage of time condensations in this cloud become the centers which gather more hydrogen to themselves, thus becoming the clouds which eventually evolve into new galaxies.

A question that occurs at once is that of the origin of these new hydrogen atoms. Where do they come from? Hoyle thinks that the matter already in existence in the universe creates in space what he calls a *creation field*, and that this causes the new atoms to come into existence. Hoyle compares this creation field to the gravitational field created by the presence of matter. He admits that the idea of a creation field is a strange idea, but he says that it can be represented by mathematical equations.

Hoyle also believes that the creation of new hydrogen atoms is the thing which causes the universe to expand. These new atoms create a pressure which results in the expansion.

Many features of the steady-state theory are startling. But so is the big-bang theory. Can astronomers decide between them? This is the subject of the next chapter.

22

The nature of the universe

Our explorations of the universe are explorations in time as well as in space. When we observe a galaxy a million light-years away, we are not seeing it as it is today. Its light took a million years to reach us. Consequently we are seeing it as it was a million years ago. When we turn a big telescope on a galaxy that is a billion light-years away, we are seeing it as it was a billion years ago. The most distant galaxies visible in the 200-inch telescope are five billion light-years away. This means that we can look backward into the universe for five billion years.

Since this is so, it should be possible to arrive at a decision between the big-bang theory and the steady-state theory. This is exactly what astronomers are now trying to do. Perhaps they will succeed in the next few years. The task, however, is an extremely difficult one. The very distant galaxies are so faint that it is difficult to photograph and study them.

The steady-state theory, as we have seen, maintains that the universe was always essentially as it is today. If this is correct, we should find the same proportion of young and old galaxies at all distances from us. But if the big-bang theory is correct, we should find old galaxies near us and younger galaxies at greater distances from us. Unfortunately we do not yet have an established theory of how galaxies change with time. In addition, the most distant galaxies are so faint that it is almost impossible to say how they differ from nearby ones.

If the steady-state theory is correct, we should find the same number of galaxies in a given volume of space, no matter how far back we go in time. We should also find the rate of expansion unchanged. The speed with which the galaxies move apart must have been the same five billion years ago as it is today.

If the big-bang theory is correct, the universe changes with time. It is an evolving universe. The galaxies must have been closer together five billion years ago than they are today. They must also have been rushing away from each other a little faster than they are today because gravitation has acted as a brake, slowing up the rate of expansion with the passage of time.

The steady-state theory leads to the conclusion that the universe is infinite and that space has zero curvature. This is sometimes called *flat space* or *Euclidean space*. With the big-bang theory, space can have positive, zero, or negative curvature. The universe is infinite if space has zero or negative curvature; it is finite if space has a positive curvature.

The big-bang theory leads to two possibilities about the future. The first is that the expansion will go on forever. In this case, the galaxies will draw farther and farther apart with the passage of time. Eventually it will be impossible to see any galaxies from the earth with the exception of the members of the Local Group. All the galaxies will grow older and older. Those that now contain gas and dust will use it up. All the stars will move off the main sequence and end up as white dwarfs. In time the universe will be cold and dark. It will be a dead universe.

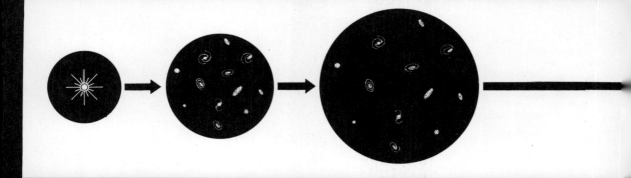

The second possibility is that the expansion is slowing down. If so, it will finally stop. As soon as expansion has stopped, gravitation will gain the upper hand. The universe will begin to contract. It will now behave like a balloon from which the air is escaping. The galaxies will approach each other, their speed growing greater as they draw closer together. Eventually all the matter of the universe will again be concentrated in the equivalent of Lemaître's primeval atom.

What will happen then? The superatom will explode and the expansion will start all over again. Astronomers speak of a universe which alternately expands and contracts as a *pulsating universe* or an *oscillating universe*. Such a universe would be infinite in time, but it would be finite in space. It would expand to a certain size and then contract to a superatom. Each cycle would begin with a big bang.

As I said, astronomers are now trying to determine which, if any, of these various possibilities is the case. All of them may eventually prove to be wrong and some new theory, not yet proposed, will give a better description of the nature of the universe.

One test of the present theories is the distribution of galaxies at

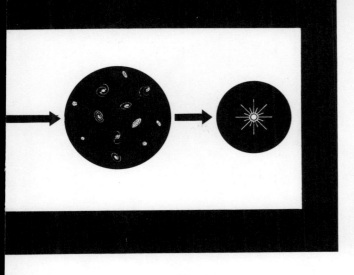

The Pulsating Universe. This theory holds that the universe alternately expands and contracts, each new cycle beginning with a "big bang."

immense distances. Martin Ryle has been studying this with the radio telescope at Cambridge, England. He concludes that the galaxies at immense distances are closer together than those near us. This is evidence in favor of the big-bang theory, for we see these distant galaxies as they were billions of years ago. The big-bang theory requires that they were closer together then.

Another test is to hunt for hydrogen clouds between the galaxies. If the steady-state theory is correct, there should be a considerable amount of hydrogen between the galaxies. There is some evidence for this. In particular, radio telescopes have disclosed that some clusters of galaxies seem to be enclosed in envelopes or halos of hydrogen gas. This, however, could be the result of the fact that all of the galaxies in the cluster evolved from one parent cloud.

The most impressive evidence to date arises from the study of the rate of expansion at immense distances from us. Astronomers have calculated what this would be for a steady-state universe and for evolving universes with positive, zero, and negative curvature.

Measurements of the red shifts of the six most distant clusters of galaxies, made at the Palomar Observatory with the 200-inch telescope, indicate that space is positive. These measurements also in-

dicate that the expansion is slowing up sufficiently to come to a stop eventually. This would mean that we live in an oscillating universe.

From a study of the rate of expansion, astronomers conclude that the universe is about 13 billion years old. This estimate may be revised before long. Some astronomers think that some of the star clusters in our own galaxy show evidence of being at least 15 billion years old.

If, indeed, the universe is an oscillating one, it may come to the end of the expanding stage in another few billion years. Then it will take 15 billion years or so to contract to a superatom. Then there will be another big bang.

A cluster of galaxies well over a billion light-years away. Studies of distant galaxies will help astronomers determine the real nature of the universe.

23

The future

Exciting days lie ahead in the world of astronomy. New instruments and new techniques may enable astronomers in the next few years to find the answers to many of the questions that are still puzzling them.

In October 1964 the Carnegie Institution of Washington announced the development of an electronic device known as the *cascaded image tube*. In principle, it is somewhat similar to the electronic camera used to pick up the scenes you see on your television set.

It is a tube five inches long and three inches in diameter. When it is placed at the eye-end of a telescope, the image formed by the telescope falls on a little glass window. The underside of the window is coated with a light-sensitive material. Electrons knocked out of the coating strike a screen across the middle of the tube, releasing a greater number of electrons from it. These strike the phosphorescent coating on another glass window at the bottom of the tube, creating an optical image which can then be photographed.

Because this image is so much brighter than the original image, the device roughly triples the power of a telescope, making a 60-inch telescope about the equivalent of a 180-inch telescope. This means that a half-dozen of the world's larger telescopes will become as powerful as the 200-inch telescope on Palomar Mountain. Certain factors complicate the use of the device with the very largest telescopes, but the 100-inch telescope will become roughly the equivalent of a 300-inch telescope, while the Palomar eye will be a 600-inch telescope in some respects.

Both the Carnegie group and scientists in other institutions are working on other electronic aids. It is possible that some day the 200-inch telescope may be the equivalent of a 1000-inch telescope.

For many years now, astronomers have been making use of the photoelectric cell or "electric eye" to measure the apparent magnitude of stars. The cell is put at the eye-end of the telescope. When the light of the star strikes the cell, it knocks electrons out of the metallic coating in the cell. This creates an electric current. The magnitude of the star can be determined from the strength of the current.

Recently, this method of determining apparent magnitudes has been greatly improved by the use of a tube known as a *photomultiplier tube*. This has a series of metallic plates in it. Electrons knocked out of the first plate strike the second one, releasing a larger number of electrons. These strike the third plate, and so on. In this way the current is amplified so that accurate determinations can be made of the magnitudes of very faint stars and galaxies.

Improvements are also being made in radio telescopes and their use. It has been found that a number of smaller reflectors can be connected together electrically to do the work of one big one. California Institute of Technology is building a group of four big "dishes," each 130 feet in diameter. These will be connected electrically to the two 90-foot dishes now in operation at the Cal Tech Radio Observatory. The sextet, operating in unison, will be more

powerful than the 250-foot radio telescope at Jodrell Bank.

The dawn of the Space Age is enabling astronomers to overcome one of the greatest handicaps of the past, the earth's atmosphere. Like the rest of us, the astronomer has to breathe air to stay alive. But otherwise the atmosphere is a great nuisance to him. The atmosphere shuts out most of the radiations from the sun and stars. Only two narrow bands of radiation can get through it. One consists of visible light and some infrared and ultraviolet light. The other consists of a narrow band of short radio waves. In addition, the earth's atmosphere contains a great deal of dust, and it is always turbulent. This constant commotion of the atmosphere blurs the images of the stars. Observatories are built on mountain tops to avoid dust and turbulence as much as possible.

Shortly after World War II, astronomers obtained better photographs of the surface of the sun and the solar spectrum by sending instruments to high altitudes with the aid of balloons and to even higher altitudes with rockets. However, a rocket remains above the atmosphere for only a few minutes.

Once satellites had been put into orbit around the earth, astronomers realized that they were ideal vehicles for carrying astronomical instruments. A number of satellites were equipped with instruments to measure the sun's output of ultraviolet light and X-rays, to analyze the streams of subatomic particles shot out by the sun, and to record the spectrum of the sun.

In March 1962, a satellite known as the Orbiting Solar Observ-

Two of the "dishes" at the California Institute of Technology. When all six are in operation, the combination will be more powerful than the huge radio telescope at Jodrell Bank.

atory (OSO) was launched by the National Aeronautics and Space Administration. Controls keep its instruments pointed at the sun. Observations are recorded on magnetic tape and transmitted to earth by radio. The NASA program provides for the launching of additional satellites of this sort.

NASA has also started the design and construction of four satellites to be known as Orbiting Astronomical Observatories (OAO's). These will carry telescopes and spectrographs into space to record ultraviolet radiations from stars. They will be controlled from the ground by radio. The first one will contain four 8-inch telescopes and one 16-inch telescope. The second will have a 36-inch telescope. It is thought that a 36-inch telescope in space may prove more powerful than the 200-inch telescope on Palomar Mountain. Eventually it is hoped to put a 50-inch telescope into space.

However, this may not be the final step. Perhaps the day will come when a 200-inch telescope will be erected in an observatory on the moon. In the first chapter of this book, I told how astronomers commute between their offices in Pasadena and the big telescopes on Mt. Wilson and Palomar Mountain. Perhaps the day is coming when they will commute between the earth and an observatory on the moon. There is no atmosphere on the moon to interfere with observations, but the astronomers will have to take along an oxygen supply for breathing purposes.

Astronomy, Hubble once wrote, is a "history of receding horizons." This book is evidence of that. We began our journey into space with the moon, 240,000 miles away. Then we proceeded to the sun, a distance of 93 million miles. We found that the nearest star was 25 trillion miles away, and that it was more convenient to measure distances within our galaxy in light-years rather than miles. We discovered that the nearest spiral galaxy is about two million light-years away, and that the farthest galaxies visible in the 200-inch telescope are five billion light-years away. Today, astronomers are hoping to double that range and reach outward— and backward—to a distance of 10 billion light-years.

This is the story of astronomy, a marvelous and magnificent achievement of the mind of man.

Table I
The Planets

Name	Average diameter (in miles)	Average distance (in millions of miles)	Period of revolution	Orbital velocity (in miles per second)	Axial rotation	Number of moons
Mercury	2,900	35.96	87.96 days	24 to 36	88 days	0
Venus	7,600	67.20	224.70 days	22	230 days(?)	0
Earth	7,913	92.90	365.25 days	18.5	23 hrs. 56 min.	1
Mars	4,200	141.6	686.98 days	15	24 hrs. 37 min.	2
Jupiter	86,800	483.3	11.86 years	8.1	9 hrs. 50 min.	12
Saturn	71,500	886.2	29.45 years	6	10 hrs. 2 min.	9
Uranus	29,400	1,783	84.01 years	4.2	10 hrs. 45 min.	5
Neptune	28,000	2,794	164.78 years	3.4	15 hrs. 48 min.(?)	2
Pluto	4,000(?)	3,670	247.69 years	?	?	0

Table II
The Brightest Stars

The table lists, in the order of their brightness, the 21 stars known as the first-magnitude stars. It also lists the latest determination of their apparent magnitudes with the photoelectric photometer. The so-called first magnitude stars actually range through three magnitudes designated at 1, 0, and −1.

The value of the apparent magnitude decreases as the brightness of the star increases.

No.	Name	Constellation	Magnitude	Color
1	Sirius	Canis Major	−1.42	White
2	Canopus	Carina	−0.72	Yellow
3	Alpha Centauri	Centaurus	−0.27	Yellow
4	Arcturus	Bootes	−0.06	Orange
5	Vega	Lyra	+0.04	White
6	Capella	Auriga	0.05	Yellow
7	Rigel	Orion	0.14	Blue
8	Procyon	Canis Minor	0.38	Yellow
9	Achernar	Eridanus	0.51	Blue
10	Beta Centauri	Centaurus	0.63	Blue

11	Betelgeuse	Orion	0.70	Red
12	Altair	Aquila	0.77	White
13	Aldebaran	Taurus	0.86	Red
14	Alpha Crucis	Crux	0.90	Blue
15	Spica	Virgo	0.91	Blue
16	Antares	Scorpio	0.92	Red
17	Pollux	Gemini	1.16	Orange
18	Fomalhaut	Piscis Austrinius	1.19	White
19	Deneb	Cygnus	1.26	White
20	Beta Crucis	Crux	1.28	Blue
21	Regulus	Leo	1.36	Blue

INDEX

INDEX

INDEX

Telescopes (*continued*)
objective of, 11
radio, 99-102, 104, 106, 129, 131
reflecting, 13, 14
refracting, 13, 15
Schmidt-type, 14, 15, 20
spectroscope attached to, 18
200-inch, of Palomar Observatory,
3-5, 6, 8-9, 13, 40, 83, 104, 122,
125
Terrestrial planets, 26
Triangulation, 70, 73
Tube, of 200-inch Palomar telescope,
5
Tycho's Nova, 52, 103

Uranus, 26, 31
Ursa Major, 60-61, 110
Ursa Minor, 89

Variable stars, 48-49, 74, 83, 90, 92
Venus, 26, 27
Virgo, 110
Visual binaries, 47, 48

Wave lengths, of light, 16, 17, 19
White light, as mixture of all colors,
16
White stars, 41, 42, 43, 65
dwarf, 42, 44, 52, 67, 68, 97, 123
giant, 67, 68

Yellow stars, 41, 43
dwarf, 44, 65, 95, 97-98
giant, 49, 67
Yerkes Observatory, 13, 14

Zero curvature, 113, 115, 123, 125